PRINCIPLES
and
PRACTICE
of
GAS CHROMATOGRAPHY

Contributors ────────────────

C. M. Drew

Chemist, Combustion Branch
U. S. Naval Ordnance Test Station
China Lake, California

S. A. Greene

Supervisor, Theoretical Chemistry Unit
Rocketdyne Research
Canoga Park, California

H. S. Knight

Chemist
Shell Development Company
Emeryville, California

H. W. Patton

Senior Research Chemist
Tennessee Eastman Company
Kingsport, Tennessee

New York · John Wiley & Sons, Inc. · London

Edited by

Robert L. Pecsok

Associate Professor of Chemistry
University of California, Los Angeles

PRINCIPLES

and

PRACTICE

of

GAS CHROMATOGRAPHY

SECOND PRINTING, OCTOBER, 1961

Copyright © 1959 by John Wiley & Sons, Inc.

Library of Congress Catalog Card Number: 59-12512

Printed in the United States of America

PREFACE

The phenomenal growth of interest in gas chromatography is reflected in many ways. Three-fourths of the
papers in the literature have appeared in the last three years.
At least fifteen companies in the United States alone now produce commercial instruments, nearly all of which have been
developed in the last three years. The fields of application
are increasing as fast as they can be counted. Confronted
with this exponential expansion, the average chemist can no
longer keep up with developments, indeed he may find it difficult to know where to begin.

In response to many requests, the University of
California, Los Angeles, offered a first course in gas chromatography February 2-6, 1959. The lecturers were asked
to summarize the material then available. Each lecture covered a particular phase (including "stationary" and "mobile")
of gas chromatography. In effect, we attempted to chromatograph all of the information and ideas available, and then
tried to isolate and expand those topics of most value to be-
ginners and to those with limited experience.

This book is an outgrowth of the course. The lec-
tures have been organized, elaborated, and edited to provide
continuity and consistency. Gas chromatography is controlled
by a veritable maze of variables, few of which can readily
be isolated for independent discussion. Thus, some duplica-
tion of material is inevitable. Wherever repetition was con-

sidered to be helpful to the reader, we have let it stand.

As in most fields of analytical chemistry, an appreciation of the basic principles is essential to the development of applications and the intelligent interpretation of the results. Therefore, the first part of this book is concerned with a discussion of theoretical principles underlying partition chromatography and a description of the mechanism of separation when the mobile phase is an inert gas. In deference to the reader who may be more interested in "how to do it", we have omitted long mathematical treatments. These chapters are followed by a more detailed description of the mobile and stationary phases. The practical details and general procedures are described in the chapters covering the effects of operational parameters, column selection and construction, sample introduction, and temperature control. General methods available for converting the experimental data into useful results are discussed in the final chapter on analytical methods.

We have not intended to review critically a large number of applications. To do this properly would require a volume several times larger than the present work. As a partial substitute, titles of all papers have been included in the extensive bibliography which is essentially complete through 1958 - plus some early 1959 references. Only a few papers in relatively inaccessible journals and papers presented at local meetings have been omitted. The list was compiled from a number of sources starting from a bibliography kindly furnished to the editor by Beckman Instruments, Inc.

Much of the material in Chapter 13 was originally prepared by Hadley Ford of the Stanford Research Institute. We wish to thank him for his cooperation. In order to make the book available before much of the material becomes superceded by newer techniques and apparatus, we have decided to reproduce the text by the photo offset method. We are greatly indebted to our typist, Nancy Hinchliff, who is responsible for the exacting preparation of the final copy.

Los Angeles, California   Robert L. Pecsok
April 1959

SYMBOLS
AND TERMS

Page numbers on which symbols are used follow each definition.

A   coefficient of eddy term in simplified van Deemter
    equation: 13, 44, 57

A   peak area, sq. cm: 124

$\underline{a}$ modified activity coefficient: 21, 63

$\underline{a}$ area of cross section of column occupied by gas
    phase: 30

B   coefficient of diffusion term in simplified van
    Deemter equation: 13, 44, 57

B   constant: 31

C   constant: 31

C   coefficient of mass transfer term in simplified
    van Deemter equation: 13, 44, 57

C_1 chart speed, cm/min: 42

C_1 — recorder sensitivity, mv/cm: 124

C_2 — detector amplification factor: 42

C_2 — chart speed, min/cm: 124

C_3 — carrier gas flow rate: 42, 124

D_{gas} — diffusion coefficient of solute in gas phase: 13, 57

D_{liq} — diffusion coefficient of solute in liquid phase: 13, 57

$\underline{d}_f$ — average thickness of liquid film: 13, 57

$\underline{d}_p$ — average particle diameter: 13, 57

F_c — volume rate of flow of carrier gas: 30, 46

g — proportionality constant: 42

H — partition coefficient, the amount of solute per unit volume of liquid phase divided by amount of solute per unit volume of gas phase: 25

H_a — equilibrium constant for adsorption: 30

HETP — height equivalent to a theoretical plate: 12, 13, 44, 57

$\underline{k}'$ — fraction of sample in liquid phase divided by fraction of sample in gas phase: 13, 57

$\underline{l}$ — length of column: 30

$\underline{m}$ — weight of sample component: 42

$\underline{m}_i$ — moles of solute $\underline{i}$:   19

$\underline{n}$ — total number of plates: 12, 18, 44, 56

$\underline{n}_a$ — moles of component adsorbed: 29

$\underline{n}_g$ moles of component in gas phase: 29

P.I.   performance index: 19

P^o vapor pressure of pure solute: 21

$\bar{p}$ average column pressure: 47

p_i column pressure at inlet: 46

p_o column pressure at outlet: 46

Q_a heat of adsorption: 30

Q_s heat of solution: 31

Q_v heat of vaporization: 31

R   gas constant: 30

r   recorder response, peak area: 42

S   sensitivity parameter: 124

s   detector sensitivity, mv/weight of solute: 42

T   absolute temperature: 30

$\underline{t}$ retention time of component (Golay):   19

$\underline{t}_a$ retention time of air: 19

$\underline{t}_R$ retention time: 12, 30, 43, 46

$\underline{u}$ linear gas velocity: 13, 44, 57

$\underline{u}$ average linear velocity of solute zone: 29

$\underline{u}_g$ linear velocity of carrier gas: 29

V^o_G interstitial volume of column: 30

V_g specific retention volume $= 273 \, H / T \rho_L$:   26

V_L volume of liquid phase in column: 31

V_R retention volume: 47, 56

V_R^o limiting (corrected) retention volume with zero pressure drop: 47

W   weight of component, mg: 124

α relative volatility: 21

α separation factor: 18

γ activity coefficient: 24, 65

γ correction factor for tortuosity of interparticle spaces: 13, 57

ΔH_v heat of vaporization: 37

Δp pressure drop across column: 19

$\Delta \underline{t}$ peak width at base: 12, 44

$\Delta \underline{t}$ peak width at half height (Golay):   19

ΔV peak width at base: 56

η fractional band impurity: 18

λ measure of packing irregularity: 13, 57

ρ_L density of liquid phase: viii

σ standard deviation: 129

TABLE OF CONTENTS

PREFACE   v

SYMBOLS AND TERMS   vii

1. INTRODUCTION,   H. W. Patton, Tennessee
   Eastman Company.   1

2. FUNDAMENTAL PRINCIPLES,   H. W. Patton,
   Tennessee Eastman Company.   8

3. MECHANISM OF SEPARATION,   H. S. Knight,
   Shell Development Company.   21

4. MOBILE PHASE,   S. A. Greene, Rocketdyne
   Research.   28

5. STATIONARY PHASE,   H. S. Knight, Shell
   Development Company.   48

6. COLUMN CONDITIONS,   H. S. Knight, Shell
   Development Company.   56

7. PEAK DISTORTIONS,   H. S. Knight, Shell
   Development Company.   63

8.   COLUMN SELECTION,   H. S. Knight, Shell
      Development Company.   69

9.   COLUMN CONSTRUCTION,   H. S. Knight,
      Shell Development Company.   83

10.   SAMPLE INTRODUCTION,   S. A. Greene
      and E. F. C. Cain, Rocketdyne Research.   86

11.   TEMPERATURE CONTROL,   C. M. Drew,
      U. S. Naval Ordnance Test Station.   97

12.   DETECTORS,   C. M. Drew, U. S. Naval
      Ordnance Test Station.   116

13.   ANALYTICAL METHODS,   R. L. Pecsok,
      University of California, Los Angeles.   135

APPENDIX I   LIST OF MANUFACTURERS.   151

          II   BIBLIOGRAPHY.   153

INDEX   223

Chapter 1

INTRODUCTION

H.W. Patton

Tennessee Eastman Company

THE MOST RECENT MEMBER of the chromatography family has a very remarkable record. It was conceived more than ten years before birth, and within seven years, it has become a tremendous giant that seems to be growing at an ever increasing rate. With proper qualification and interpretation, the sentences above describe the history of gas-liquid chromatography. The principles of this method were clearly described by Martin and Synge in 1941 in a paper devoted primarily to the introduction of another kind of chromatography (5). The idea of using a gaseous moving phase, which later proved to be so valuable, was apparently not exploited until James and Martin published their classical paper in 1952 (44).

Historical Background. Chromatographic methods can be subdivided according to the physical nature of the phases and to the separation mechanism involved. As a background for the discussion of gas chromatography, a tabulation of various kinds of chromatography is given in Table 1-1.

Although several workers preceded Tswett with methods that might be called chromatography, he is generally given credit for inventing the method (140). He obtained some separations that were quite remarkable at the time (1903). For example, he separated the extract of green

1

TABLE 1-1   CHROMATOGRAPHIC METHODS

Liquid Phase Column Chromatography	
Adsorption	Tswett, 1903
Partition	Martin and Synge, 1941
Ion-Exchange	Various Workers, 1947
Paper Chromatography	Consden, Gordon and Martin, 1944
Gas Chromatography	
Adsorption	Hesse, 1942
Partition	James and Martin, 1952

leaves into several components by pouring the solution onto one end of a column of adsorbent and then passing fresh solvent through the column. The material initially forming a green band at the top of the column was caused to move down the column and form several bands having various shades of green and yellow. Because his separations involved colored materials, Tswett called the process "chromatography". The term "chromatography" as used today is generally a misnomer, but it is well established and it is unlikely that it will be replaced by a more descriptive name.

In spite of the simplicity and power of Tswett's methods, they were used very little until 1931 when Kuhn and Lederer used chromatography to separate α- and β-carotene. The results of this work were soon well known and highly regarded. Many workers in several countries experimented with chromatographic methods, and the field developed rapidly.

DESCRIPTION OF METHODS

It is difficult to devise a simple definition of chromatography that includes all chromatographic processes and excludes other separatory processes. Perhaps it is sufficient to outline some of the features of common chromatographic methods.

All chromatographic methods involve distribution of the material to be separated between two phases which move with respect to each other. Generally one phase is fixed and the other is mobile. The fixed phase must be solid or liquid, otherwise it cannot be conveniently held fixed. The mobile phase can be either a liquid or a gas. Thus, there are four kinds of chromatography according to the kinds of fixed and mobile phases used.

Any chromatographic method that uses a gaseous mobile phase is called gas chromatography. The nature of the fixed phase is the basis for two major subdivisions. If the fixed phase is a solid, such as activated charcoal, the method is called gas-solid chromatography (abbreviated GSC). The term gas-liquid chromatography (GLC) or gas-liquid partition chromatography, applies when the fixed phase is a liquid. Generally the fixed liquid is used as a thin film on solid particles or on the inner wall of a capillary column.

Gas chromatographic methods can also be classified according to the means of moving the sample through the column. Elution, displacement and frontal analysis are the most commonly employed methods. All three methods can be used with adsorption columns (GSC), but only elution is applicable to partition columns (GLC).

Frontal Analysis. During a frontal analysis, the mixture to be analyzed (suitably diluted in a carrier gas in some cases) is passed continuously through a column of adsorbent. The components emerge from the column in the order of their relative affinities for the adsorbent, but only the first one is separated from all other sample components. Ideally, a plot of concentration versus time for sample components in the column effluent is like that shown in Fig. 1-1. Of course, an indiscriminate detector such as a thermal conductivity cell records only the heavy profile line and does not indicate the concentrations of individual components. Because of displacement effects, the concentration of a given component in the effluent usually decreases as other components appear.

Interpretation of the experimental curve for the purpose of identification and determination of the components present is possible but rather complicated compared to displacement or elution.

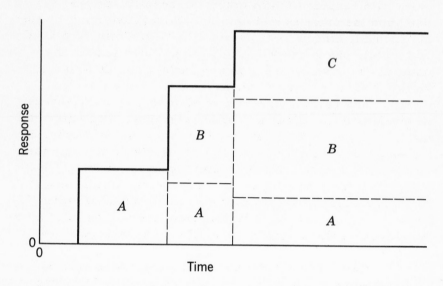

Fig. 1-1.   Chromatogram for ideal frontal analysis.

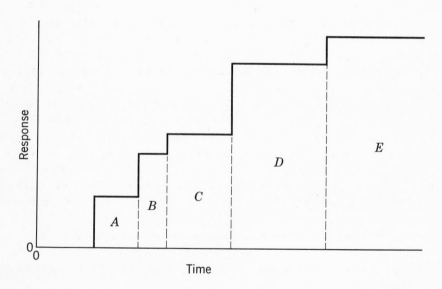

Fig. 1-2.   Chromatogram for ideal displacement analysis.

Displacement Analysis. The essential features of displacement analysis are as follows. The sample is put on one end of a column of adsorbent. A carrier gas containing the vapor of a substance more strongly adsorbed than any sample component is passed through the column. This substance displaces the sample from the adsorbent and each sample component in turn displaces others that are less strongly adsorbed. The components arrange themselves in well defined zones in order of increasing affinity for the adsorbent and eventually move to the end of the column where they emerge in succession. A plot of concentration versus time for an ideal displacement analysis is shown in Fig. 1-2. The height of a given step is the means of qualitative identification. The length of the step is proportional to the amount of material that produced it, with a different proportionality constant for each substance.

Of course, there is always a region between adjacent components that contains a mixture of the two. However, it is generally possible to arrange experimental parameters so that the amount of material in this region of mixing is a small portion of the total.

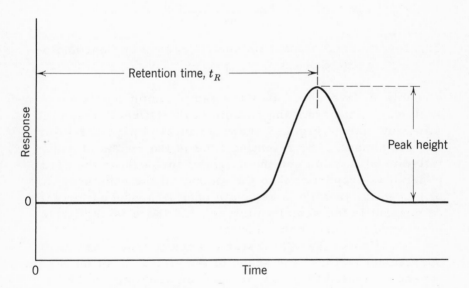

Fig. 1-3. Chromatogram for ideal elution of one component.

Elution. Elution involves passing a carrier gas continuously through the chromatographic system. A gaseous
or volatile liquid sample is introduced into this gas stream
and carried onto the column of adsorbent. Each sample component distributes itself in a characteristic manner between
the gaseous phase and the fixed phase (solid or liquid), and
that portion in the gaseous phase moves with the carrier

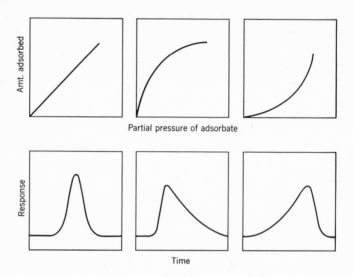

Fig. 1-4. Typical isotherms and corresponding chromato-
           graphic peaks.

stream. In favorable cases the sample components are separated and pass from the column in the effluent stream at
different times. Fig. 1-3 shows an ideal elution curve for
one component. The retention time is the means of qualitative identification and the height of the peak or the area
under it is proportional to the amount of the substance that
produced it. Ideally, a separate peak is produced for each
component in the sample mixture, and there is negligible
overlap of adjacent components.

Unless there is distortion due to instrumental or
operational factors, the shape of the elution peak for a component is related to its adsorption (or solution) isotherm.
Three common types of isotherms and the corresponding

elution peaks are shown in Fig. 1-4. The symmetrical peak which is associated with a linear isotherm is the most desirable for analytical purposes. Some asymmetry can be tolerated, but if it is excessive, the components move in overlapping zones of low concentration.

Unfortunately, for the purposes of gas-solid elution chromatography, isotherms for the adsorption of most substances are not linear but resemble the center example of Fig. 1-4. Consequently, elution from adsorbents generally results in peaks with sharp "fronts" and long "tails". Nevertheless, elution from adsorbents produces usable chromatograms in many cases, and there are a few examples of adsorbents that produce highly symmetrical peaks (657).

Symmetrical or nearly symmetrical elution peaks are rather common in gas-liquid chromatography. Non-ideal solutions can, however, result in asymmetry of either the "tailing" (Fig. 1-4, center) or "leading" type (Fig. 1-4, right). In gas-liquid systems, adsorption of the sample components by the solid material supporting the fixed liquid sometimes occurs to such an extent that severe tailing results. Peak distortions are discussed in more detail in Chapter 7.

Chapter **2**

FUNDAMENTAL
PRINCIPLES

H. W. Patton

Tennessee Eastman Company

GAS-LIQUID METHODS are undoubtedly applicable to a wider variety of problems than are adsorption methods. This fact is due in part to the sharp symmetrical peaks usually produced and also to the tremendous variety of liquids that can be used to obtain the desired selectivity. Because of the much greater importance of gas-liquid methods in practice, some time will be spent discussing the mechanism of separation on this type of column, and some of the factors affecting the efficiency of separation will be considered. A part of what will be said is also applicable to adsorption columns with elution development.

PARTITION CHROMATOGRAPHY

If a gas-liquid column is visualized as operating in a manner somewhat analogous to a distillation column, a theoretical plate treatment like that first described by Martin and Synge (5) is applicable. A theoretical plate is defined as a section of the column in which the vapor leaving the section has the composition that would be in equilibrium with the average concentration of liquid solution within the section. In the process of passing through one theoretical plate the equivalent of one equilibration between the liquid phase and vapor phase occurs.

8

The over-all separation achieved with a column depends on two things - separation per plate (separation factor) and the number of plates. The separation produced by
one equilibration is determined primarily by the nature of
the high-boiling liquid, the nature of the components to be
separated, and the temperature. The number of theoretical
plates in a column of given dimensions depends in a rather
complicated way on many factors, for example, rates of diffusion in the two phases, thickness of liquid layer, uniformity of column packing, nature of carrier gas, and flow rate
of carrier gas. The number of effective theoretical plates
is increased by an increase in column length, within limits,
and decreased slightly by an increase in column diameter.

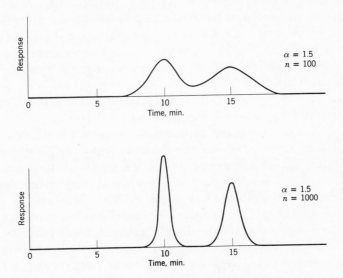

Fig. 2-1. Hypothetical chromatogram illustrating effect of
          separation factor and number of theoretical plates
          on degree of separation.

In terms of a chromatogram of two components the
separation factor is equal to the ratio of the two retention
times. The sharpness of the peaks is a measure of the number of theoretical plates. For example, Fig. 2-1 shows two
hypothetical chromatograms, for each of which the separation factor is 1.5. However, the separation is greatly im-

proved in the lower example because of the greater number
of theoretical plates. In principle, the separation of two
substances can be improved either by using a column liquid
with better selectivity (larger separation factor) or by operating the column so as to increase the number of theoretical
plates. In practice, the selectivity of the column liquid can
be used to advantage except when the substances to be separated are very similar. Of course, it is generally desirable
to operate with as many theoretical plates as possible, consistent with other requirements.

<u>Selectivity of the Column Liquid.</u> Final choice of a
column liquid with suitable selectivity for a given separation
is generally based on actual chromatographic experiments
with materials considered to be good prospects. Although
separation factors can be evaluated from static distribution
studies, it is generally easier to prepare a column and to
test its chromatographic behavior than to evaluate it by other means. However, even crude knowledge of intermolecu-
lar interactions is a help in choosing the substances to be
tested. To illustrate qualitatively the sort of effects that
are encountered, some examples will be given.

When a mixture of benzene and cyclohexane are put
through a column in which the column liquid is hexadecane
or paraffin oil, the benzene precedes the cyclohexane. If,
under the same conditions, a column containing tricresyl
phosphate or benzylbiphenyl is used, the cyclohexane precedes the benzene. Generally, column liquids containing
aromatic rings selectively detain aromatic compounds.

Polar liquids interact preferentially with polar
sample components. The retardation of polar vapors is particularly important when hydrogen bonding is involved. For
example, water and alcohols are selectively detained on
columns containing glycerol or ethylene glycol.

Specific interactions leading to weak complex formation sometimes cause excellent selectivity. For example,
ethylene glycol saturated with silver nitrate can be used to
separate alkenes and dienes from the corresponding alkanes.
The unsaturated compounds are also separated from one
another in many cases because of their different degrees of
interaction with the silver ions. Alkynes interact very
strongly with the silver ions probably forming acetylides

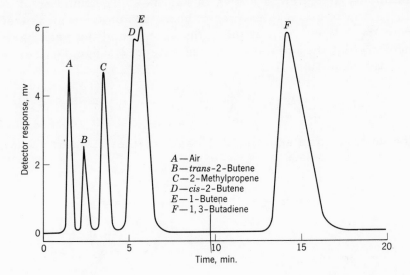

Fig. 2-2. Chromatogram of C_4 hydrocarbons using a column containing ethylene glycol saturated with silver nitrate.

which remain on the column. The elution curve for a sample of hydrocarbons from a silver nitrate-ethylene glycol column at room temperature is shown in Fig. 2-2.

Even with such similar substances as meta- and para-xylene, the separation factor can be varied somewhat by using different column liquids (673). The subtle solvent-solute interactions responsible for this behavior are not understood.

THEORETICAL PLATE TREATMENT

The number of theoretical plates can be calculated from several expressions which do not necessarily give the same results. However, each is essentially a measure of the peak sharpness, and all give about the same relative values. The carrier gas can be considered to move inter-mittently from plate to plate, as in the original treatment of Martin and Synge (5), or continuously as assumed by Glueckauf (117). The relative peak width can be evaluated in several ways (5, 143, 698). The method of calculation

commonly accepted is shown in Fig. 2-3. The number of
plates, $\underline{n}$, is given in terms of the retention time measured
from the introduction of the sample, t_R, and the peak base
measured at the points where the extended tangents inter-
sect the base line, $\Delta \underline{t}$.

$$\underline{n} = 16 \left(\frac{t_R}{\Delta \underline{t}} \right)^2 \qquad (2-1)$$

The units used in equation 2-1 can be either time or volume

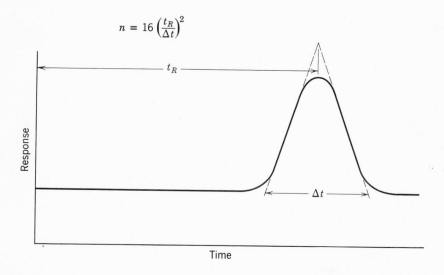

Fig. 2-3.   Recommended method for calculating number of
theoretical plates.

as long as they are consistent. The height equivalent to a
theoretical plate (HETP) is obtained by dividing the column
length by the number of plates. It is worthwhile to note that
HETP, which one might naively assume to be independent
of retention time, generally decreases with increasing retention time. However, HETP may increase with increasing column length. Low values of HETP correspond to efficient column operation.

The plate theory provides a very useful means of evaluating column efficiency, but it does not help the experimenter decide how to operate his column so as to obtain best efficiency. The so-called rate theory of van Deemter is a very useful basis for considering the effects of several column and operational parameters (316). The van Deemter equation in its complete and simplified forms is shown below.

$$\text{HETP} = 2\lambda\underline{d_p} + \frac{2\gamma D_{gas}}{\underline{u}} + \frac{8\ \underline{k}'}{\pi^2(1 + \underline{k}')^2}\ \frac{\underline{d_f}^2}{D_{liq}}\ \underline{u} \quad (2\text{-}2)$$

$$\text{HETP} = \text{A} + \text{B}/\underline{u} + \text{C}\underline{u} \quad (2\text{-}3)$$

Eddy Diffusion	Molecular Diffusion	Resistance to Mass Transfer

The HETP is, of course, the height equivalent to a theoretical plate, and it is almost invariably computed from equation 2-1. Other symbols in the equation are: λ, a quantity characteristic of the packing; $\underline{d_p}$, average particle diameter; γ, a correction factor for the tortuosity of the interparticle spaces; D_{gas}, diffusion coefficient in the gas phase; $\underline{u}$, linear gas velocity; $\underline{k}'$, fraction of sample in liquid phase divided by the fraction in the vapor phase; $\underline{d_f}$, thickness of liquid film; and D_{liq}, diffusion coefficient in liquid phase.

The van Deemter theory is concerned with the influences which tend to broaden chromatographic bands as they move down the column. According to the theory there are three such factors which are called eddy diffusion, molecular diffusion, and resistance to mass transfer. The eddy diffusion contribution results from the irregular paths the gas takes through the packed column. These paths have different lengths, cross sections, and directions. As a result of these irregularities the chromatographic band is spread along the column. The two factors, other than the numerical constant in the eddy diffusion term are $\underline{d_p}$, the average particle diameter, and λ, a quantity characteristic of the packing. Reducing the particle size should decrease the eddy diffusion contribution to HETP. Uniformity of particle size and proper packing help to reduce λ.

Molecular diffusion of the sample molecules in the carrier gas is the second cause of band broadening. The

contribution to HETP from this factor increases with decreasing molecular weight of the carrier gas. Thus nitrogen, argon and carbon dioxide are preferable to hydrogen
and helium with regard to column efficiency. Diffusion decreases with increasing pressure of the carrier gas. Increasing temperature increases diffusion.

   The term designated resistance to mass transfer
involves several parameters. $\underline{k}'$ is the ratio of the amount
of sample dissolved in the liquid phase to that in the gaseous
phase. Its value depends on the partition coefficient and the
relative volumes occupied by liquid and gas in the column.
Generally $\underline{k}'$ is greater than one, and under this circum-
stance increasing $\underline{k}'$ reduces HETP. Thus it is expected
that components with greater solubility in the liquid phase
will lead to somewhat smaller HETP.

   The effective thickness of the liquid film, $\underline{d_f}$, appears to the second power in the expression and, hence,
would be expected to be an important factor. Reducing $\underline{d_f}$
increases column efficiency. However, if this result is
achieved by decreasing the amount of liquid in the column,
$\underline{k}'$ is decreased, thereby partially counteracting the improve-
ment. Furthermore, with a porous support like kieselguhr,
it is likely that beyond a certain limit, further reduction in
the amount of liquid simply causes incomplete coverage of
the surface rather than complete coverage by a thinner layer.

   The liquid diffusion coefficient $D_{liq.}$ is affected by
the viscosity of the column liquid. In some cases increased
temperature may improve separations by decreasing the
viscosity of the column liquid. Since other factors ($\underline{k}'$ and
D_{gas}) are adversely affected, increased temperature may
decrease column efficiency.

   The factor in the van Deemter equation which has
not been discussed yet is the flow rate of the carrier gas,
$\underline{u}$. For discussion of the effect of flow rate it is convenient
to consider the simplified form of the equation. It is apparent that eddy diffusion is independent of flow rate, the contribution to HETP from molecular diffusion is inversely
proportional to flow rate, and resistance to mass transfer
contributes in direct proportion to flow rate. From this
relation it is expected that, if all other factors are constant,
there will be an optimum flow rate for most efficient column
operation. Fig. 2-4 shows the form of the relation graphi-

cally. At flow rates below the optimum, molecular diffusion makes a large contribution to HETP, and above the optimum, resistance to mass transfer is an important factor. For gases of high diffusivity, for example hydrogen and helium, the molecular diffusion contribution is particularly likely to be important. If the film of liquid is thick or of high viscosity, resistance to mass transfer may be dominant. Perhaps it is worthwhile to discuss one more point in connection with Fig. 2-4. Gases are compressible, and the pressure at the inlet end of a chromatographic column is greater than that at the outlet. It follows that the flow rate of carrier gas is always greater at the outlet end than at the inlet end. As a result, the column cannot operate at the optimum flow rate throughout its entire length. For columns of low pressure drop, this factor is of little importance. For columns containing very small particles of packing material, the pressure drop may be such that some parts of the column operate at very inefficient flow rates. Increasing the absolute pressure at both ends of the column decreases the ratio of inlet to outlet pressures and, hence, leads to a more uniform flow rate along the column. A correction factor is given in Chapter 4 for converting observed retention volumes

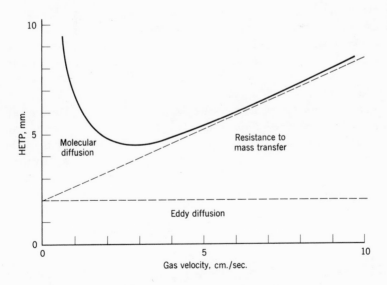

Fig. 2-4. Influence of carrier gas velocity on column efficiency.

to corrected volumes which are independent of the pressure.

There is a method, which has apparently not been used, to provide a constant linear velocity of carrier gas along the column. This result can be achieved, in principle, by varying the column diameter to compensate for pressure changes. An ideal column built on this principle would taper from the inlet to the outlet with a continuously increasing diameter. The ratio of the outlet diameter to the inlet diameter should equal the square root of the ratio of the inlet to outlet pressures. In practice, a column with this internal geometry would be difficult to fabricate. However, columns made of short sections of straight tubing with increasing diameters would approximate the desired geometry. If the ratio of inlet to outlet pressures can be reduced to less than two, the problem is no longer significant.

Qualitative expectation from the rate theory are summarized in Table 2-1.

TABLE 2-1.   QUALITATIVE PREDICTIONS FROM RATE THEORY.

Change	Partial Effects	Effect on HETP
Particle Size		
Increase	Increase d_p, decrease λ?	?
Narrow range	Decrease λ, γ	Decrease
Spherical	Decrease λ, γ	Decrease
Carrier Gas		
Increase density	Decrease D_{gas}	Decrease
Increase pressure	Decrease D_{gas}	Decrease
Increase flow rate		Minimum at optimum flow rate
Temperature		
Increase	Increase D_{gas}, D_{liq}, decrease k'	?
Liquid		
Decrease amount	Decrease k', d_f	Decrease
Decrease viscosity	Increase D_{liq}	Decrease

It is apparent that optimum separation of a sample is seldom achieved by simply packing a column with whatever is handy and operating it by rule-of-thumb. To find the optimum combination of all the variables involved by means of experiments designed for proper statistical analysis would be a considerable task. Evidently, no one has attempted so complete an analysis of any system. Fortunately, most analytical separations are achieved with little consideration for efficiency. Nevertheless, theory has been useful in cases where high efficiency was necessary, and also some improved rules-of-thumb have resulted from experimental work designed to test theory.

Experimental Tests of Rate Theory. Most of the studies conducted so far have been concerned with investigating the change in HETP as a result of changes in particle size and uniformity, ratio of liquid to solid, temperature, nature of the carrier gas and flow rate of carrier gas. In general, the van Deemter equation has been found consistent with experimental results. Bohemen and Purnell (540) have some indication that the eddy diffusion term is inversely proportional to flow rate rather than independent of flow rate. Other workers have generally found the form of the equation to be essentially correct.

Several recent papers have been devoted to investigation of the factors affecting column efficiency. There is general agreement that use of hydrogen or helium as carrier gas results in less efficient column operation than when nitrogen or argon is used. In spite of this fact hydrogen and helium are still widely used because they result in good sensitivity for thermal conductivity detectors.

Use of smaller particles of support material has been found to give better efficiency in practice. It is particularly important to use particles of uniform size. There is rather general agreement that column efficiency increases with decreasing ratio of high-boiling liquid to solid support. There is evidently a limit below which adsorption becomes important, but several workers have found increasing efficiency with amounts of liquid down to about 2%. With "lean" columns only extremely small samples can be used. Column efficiency increases with decreasing sample size.

The use of higher than atmospheric pressure in a chromatographic column improves efficiency for two reasons. First, molecular diffusion is reduced because of increased density of the carrier gas. Second, at a given pressure drop across the column, the flow rate of carrier gas is more uniform (640). Further tests of the rate theory are described in Chapter 6.

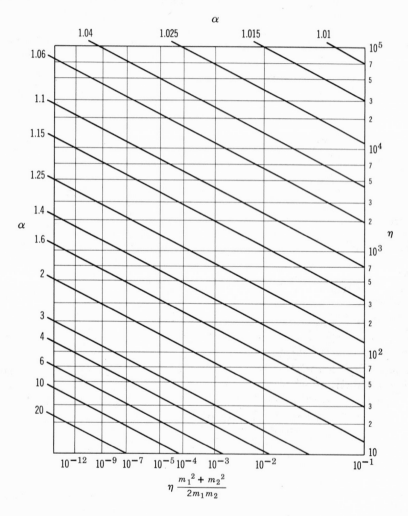

Fig. 2-5.   Number of theoretical plates ($\underline{n}$) and separation
          factor (α) required to give fractional band im-
          purity (η).   After Glueckauf (117).

The relation among separation factor, number of theoretical plates, and degree of separation has been worked out by Glueckauf (117). The results can be presented in the form of a very useful graph like that shown in Fig. 2-5. The number of theoretical plates $\underline{n}$ is plotted versus the factor $\eta \, (m_1^2 + m_2^2)/ \, 2m_1 m_2$ where η is the fractional impurity in each separated fraction and m_1 and m_2 are the respective numbers of moles of the two substances in the mixture to be separated. A straight line is obtained for each separation factor and the lines for different separation factors are parallel.

Use of the graph will be illustrated by means of an example. Suppose that two substances have a separation factor (ratio of retention times) of 2.0, and that they are present in a 1:1 ratio. For this case $m_1 = m_2$ and the factor $\eta \, (m_1^2 + m_2^2)/ \, 2m_1 m_2$ is equal to η. One can determine from the graph the number of plates required to produce the desired purity. A fractional impurity of 1% (0.01) would require about 45 plates or the fractional impurity could be reduced to 10^{-5} by use of a column with 150 theoretical plates. If the substances are present in a 10:1 molar ratio, $\eta \, (m_1^2 + m_2^2)/ \, 2 \, m_1 m_2 = 5.05$, and the number of plates required to obtain a fractional impurity of 10^{-5} is about 120. For a molar ratio of 100:1, about 90 plates are required for the same fractional impurity.

PERFORMANCE INDEX

In connection with the theory of gas chromatography in open capillary tubes, Golay has proposed the use of the Performance Index, which is calculated as follows (577):

$$\text{P. I.} = \frac{(\Delta \underline{t})^4 \; t_a \; \Delta \underline{p}}{\underline{t}^3 \, (\underline{t} \; - \; 15 \, \underline{t}_a/16)}$$

$\Delta \underline{t}$ is the peak width at half height, $\underline{t}$ is the retention time of a sample component, $\underline{t}_a$ is the retention time of air, and $\Delta \underline{p}$ is the pressure drop across the column.

Originally the Performance Index was introduced as a measure of "the intrinsic goodness of capillary columns operated at optimum flow rate." According to Golay the theoretical lower limit of the value of the Performance

Index is 0. 1 poise. The smallest value obtained for actual capillary columns is 2. 3 (577). For packed columns, the smallest value reported is 5. 55 (640).

Chapter **3**

MECHANISM
OF SEPARATION

H. S. Knight

Shell Devolopment Company

AT THIS POINT it would be well to recall that there are two
basic kinds of gas chromatography. One, called gas-solid
chromatography (GSC), achieves a separation as a result of
the varying adsorbability of the components of a mixture on
some adsorbent. The other, called gas-liquid chromatography (GLC), is based on varying absorbability of the sample
components in a liquid solvent impregnated on a support.

RELATIVE VOLATILITY

The separation in gas chromatography (GSC or GLC)
takes place because the molecules of one component spend
more time in the carrier gas than those of another, hence
the former material is swept through the column faster. It
is apparent then that separation is a matter of relative volatility (292). One factor that obviously affects the volatility
is the vapor pressure, P^O. Other factors include adsorption
and solute-solvent effects, and in some cases molecular
weight. In the equation below, the relative volatility, α, is
expressed in the usual manner as for distillation, but the
activity coefficients are replaced by the non-committal $\underline{a}$'s,
where $\underline{a}$ includes any factor affecting the volatility, and
hence the separation, except vapor pressure.

$$\alpha = \frac{\underline{a}_2 P^O_2}{\underline{a}_1 P^O_1} = \frac{\text{Retention Time 1}}{\text{Retention Time 2}}$$

This equation will be used to interpret GSC and GLC separations as well as asymmetrical peaks. If the vapor pressures are known only the retention times need be obtained for calculation of $\underline{a}$ values. If $\underline{a}$ values for various columns are available, one giving a desired relative volatility can be selected. The retention times in the above equation must be corrected for the void space in the column, which is done automatically if they are measured from a peak representing an unabsorbed, unadsorbed material, such as air in GLC.

Application to Adsorption. In the adsorption or GSC case, $\underline{a}$ represents adsorbability primarily. On polar adsorbents there is a general agreement between adsorbability and the polarity of the molecule, where polarity may be measured by dipole moments or dielectric constants, or by solubility in polar solvents such as water. Amines, water and alcohols are most strongly adsorbed, followed by carbonyls, acids, esters, ethers, aromatics, olefins and saturates. The higher the molecular weight the lower the polarity and adsorbability. Among the hydrocarbons, degree of unsaturation can be correlated with adsorbability. Thus dienes are more strongly held than monoolefins, and highly unsaturated compounds like cyclopentadiene are more strongly held than benzene. The ring or chain structure also plays a role. In liquid phase work solute-solvent interactions can reverse the sequence, for example methyl alcohol is adsorbed from dilute solution in n-heptane (95). This causes the well known S-shaped adsorption isotherms. In GSC such interactions are negligible. In GSC the paraffin is always preferentially removed from a blend with a cyclane of the same carbon number, and methyl alcohol is more strongly adsorbed than n-heptane on polar adsorbents.

Nonpolar adsorbents such as activated carbon are also used in GSC. On carbon the adsorption of hydrocarbons is strong, and increases rapidly with molecular weight, so that this adsorbent is seldom used for C_2's and never for C_3's as far as the author is aware. The affinity of carbon for hydrocarbons is shown by the fact that methane emerges after carbon monoxide from a carbon column.

In practice, GSC is used almost exclusively for fixed gases. However, the adsorption of higher boiling compounds should be understood because adsorption affects GLC separations in ways that will be taken up later.

In gas analysis, the vapor pressure ratio in the relative volatility equation is neglected because the column is practically always operated above the critical temperature. It is probably easier to determine the remaining a_2/a_1 ratio by GSC than to apply data from other sources to column selection.

There is one predictable factor that influences GSC separations to some extent, namely the molecular weights of the components. Large molecules are likely to diffuse into and out of the pores of the adsorbent more slowly than light ones. This effect becomes more important as the pores become deeper, particularly if the mouth of the pore is restricted.

An outstanding, relatively new class of polar adsorbents having pores with restricted openings is the Molecular Sieve series made by Linde Air Products. In the gas analysis work of Davis and Schreiber, described later, the molecular weight sequence is usually adhered to. Methane emerges before carbon monoxide on this support.

The Molecular Sieves influence separation in one other very important way, by excluding molecules that are too large to enter. The most common sieve in GSC is the 5A grade, having pores about 5 angstroms in diameter. Such pores will admit normal paraffins but will not admit branched chain compounds. Since petroleum products contain large amounts of normals, the 5A sieves are of great importance in the petroleum industry. For example, the normals are of low octane number and their determination in gasoline is of interest. Brenner and Coates (544) removed the normal paraffins from a C_4-C_{11} stream, using one foot of 5A sieve and a long partition column. They determined the normals by difference. Whitham (659) worked with higher boiling fractions, as will be discussed later.

Application to Partition. The mechanism of separation in GLC will now be discussed. In this case $\underline{a}$ represents primarily the activity coefficient of the sample component in the solvent. It is customary, though not always justified, to assume that there is no adsorption. The relative volatility equation then becomes (as in distillation):

$$\alpha = \frac{\gamma_2 P^o_2}{\gamma_1 P^o_1}$$

In GLC vapor pressure is very important, since the samples commonly have a critical temperature above room temperature. The two parameters, γ and P, are responsible at the same time for the scope and the complexity of GLC. The γ is the Raoult's law deviation factor, and it expresses the tendency of the solute molecules to escape from the solution to a greater or lesser extent than would be expected from their concentration and the vapor pressure of the pure solute. The γ ratio is a measure of the selectivity of the column for compounds 1 and 2.

Chromatographic Columns versus Distillation Columns. The question might arise as to why with modern columns having very large numbers of plates (high efficiency) there should be much interest in selectivity. In the first place, GLC plates are not to be compared directly with distillation plates. In a distillation column there is a uniform gradation of the volatile material from a low concentration at the bottom to a high concentration at the top. Each plate contributes something to the separation. In GLC the sample components pass through the column in a band which never under ordinary conditions fills the entire column. Only a small part of the column is actually engaged in separating the sample at any one time. Then the highly efficient columns have drawbacks in terms of convenience and analytical time, and will probably be used only where needed. The variables affecting efficiency are discussed in Chapters 2 and 6.

Further, selectivity is of interest in trace analysis. In this case large samples are necessary, and if the trace material can be made to emerge early, it will not be on the tail of the large peak. Ideally, it will form a relatively high, narrow peak which can be easily distinguished and measured.

Finally, there will always be cases where two or more materials have the same retention time on a particular solvent. This will occur whenever $\underline{a}_2/\underline{a}_1 = P^o_1/P^o_2$.

GLC is an analytical scale extractive distillation in that both vapor pressure and solvent-solute interactions can influence the result. Vapor pressure data for use in the relative volatility equation are available from Jordan's book (94) or from API tables for hydrocarbons and simple derivatives. Pierotti et al. (287) have worked out an empirical method for calculating activity coefficients which might be used for a preliminary selection of promising columns. Their method is good to about 5%, but since GLC will separate materials whose volatilities differ less than 5%, final column selection is often empirical. The above approach assumes that adsorption is negligible. All in all, it is more likely that GLC will be used to calculate relative volatilities than that these will be available for use in column selection.

GLC normally involves volatile solutes and non-volatile solvents, whereas in normal distillation the components for which relative volatility data are most needed will have similar volatilities. However, Kwantes and Rijnders (606) have shown that γ values can be determined by GLC where the solvent is only one carbon number different from the solute. They achieved this by saturating the carrier with the solvent to reduce loss during the experiment. They experienced some difficulty with adsorption. Their best results were obtained with nonpolar solutes in polar solvents (see Chapter 7).

Solute-Solvent Interaction. It is of interest to consider the order of magnitude of the activity coefficient ratio change with solvent. Taking water and n-heptane as an extreme example, the retention time ratio of these compounds will vary by a factor of 1000 as the solvent is changed from a hydrocarbon to glycerol. It will be shown shortly that among the C_6 hydrocarbons the naphthenes and paraffins may be shifted relatively by a factor of 3, the saturates and olefins by a factor of 2, and the saturates and aromatics by some 15 times.

Before going briefly into the nature of the interactions causing high or low γ values, it should be pointed out that GLC literature data will seldom be given in terms of relative volatilities. It is considered that the most common reason for consulting the literature will be to obtain information from which one can reproduce a given reported separation. The quantity best meeting this need is the partition coefficient H (not to be confused with the H in HETP) or a closely related quantity V_g , the specific retention volume. Detailed discussions of terms, units and methods of pre-senting data have been given by Ambrose, Keulemans and Purnell (529) and by Johnson and Stross (598). Many prac-tical gas chromatographers will probably continue to think in terms of retention times or inches of chart.

Since activity coefficients will seldom be available with sufficient accuracy to permit selection of a specific solvent for a given difficult separation, it is important to know how to proceed if the column being tried is unsatisfac-tory from the standpoint of selectivity. In general, the ap-proach is to vary the solvent's affinity for the solutes in a systematic way to improve the separation.

Keulemans, Kwantes and Zaal (136, 439) have dis-cussed the problem more or less from this point of view. The forces affecting solubility include (1) forces between permanent dipoles, (2) forces between a permanent and an induced dipole, and (3) nonpolar forces. These concepts are readily used to explain the variation in separation of cyclohexane and benzene as the solvent increases in polarity.

On a paraffin (nonpolar) solvent, benzene emerges earlier than cyclohexane because the benzene molecules do not interact with each other as they do in pure benzene. Hence benzene in dilute solution in paraffin assumes a lower boiling point, in accord with its lower molecular weight, and benzene emerges ahead of cyclohexane. On a phthalate ester solvent benzene becomes polarized, its activity coef-ficient goes down, and it emerges after cyclohexane.

A common interaction is the hydrogen bond. With a polyglycol solvent the primary, secondary and tertiary amines form successively weaker hydrogen bonds (higher activity coefficients) whereas a paraffin solvent separates them by boiling point.

In the previous discussion selectivity has been pre-sented in terms of activity coefficients. In the literature other ways of showing selectivity are common. The boiling point or vapor pressure or carbon number may be plotted against the log of the retention time, retention volume, or H value, for various homologous series. The result is a series of lines or gentle curves, which differ on the time axis according to selectivity. An interesting way to com-pare two solvents is to plot the log of the partition coeffi-

cient obtained on one against similar data for the other. A
series of parallel lines is obtained (287) for the various homologous series. One point for a new series establishes the
line for that series. However, on any of these plots the first
few members may be out of line.

Instead of plotting retention time or partition coefficients, relative times are often used. Tenney (649) used
n-pentane as a standard with an assigned time of unity, and
calculated the retention times of other materials on this basis. Similarly, Knight (603) used 1-hexene or methyl alcohol as a standard having an assigned a value of unity. The
use of a standard can simplify column comparisons within
any one laboratory, although there are valid arguments
against this practice if the data are to be published.

In this chapter we have emphasized selectivity, but
of course there are occasions when nothing more is desired
than a good boiling point separation. In practice something
in between is often the best. Consider the slide rule, one
portion of which can be moved relative to the rest. So it is
with selective solvents - one molecular type spectrum can
be moved relative to the others. If sufficient selectivity is
available complete separation will result. The separation
within each type will be more or less by boiling point. In
many cases, however, the movement is small and one set
of unresolved peaks is simply exchanged for another set.
If the sample is not too complex it may be possible to control the selectivity so that peaks of one type appear among
peaks of the others without actually conflicting. Examples
of this and other approaches will be taken up in Chapter 8.

Chapter 4

MOBILE PHASE

S. A. Greene

Rocketdyne Research

IN CONSIDERING THE TYPES OF GASES which could serve as carriers, one must first determine the role of the mobile phase. The theory of gas-liquid chromatography developed by Martin and Synge (5) introduces hardly any new concepts differing from those of liquid chromatography. It has been suggested that gas chromatography differs from liquid chromatography only in that the mobile phase is compressible (44) and the carrier gas undergoes an acceleration through a packed column. The advantages of a gas as a mobile phase are the following (243): (a) high rates of diffusion in the gas phase allow equilibrium with the liquid to be rapidly attained, (b) the compressibility of the gas allows the convenience of long thin columns even at rapid rates of flow, (c) it is easier to detect vapors in permanent gases than solutes in solvents, particularly in the case of such unreactive substances as saturated hydrocarbons, (d) high column efficiencies are attainable even at rapid rates of flow, so that precise separations can be carried out more rapidly than by any other technique.

THEORETICAL CONSIDERATIONS

The mechanism of separation of gases by gas chromatography and the function of the carrier are quite amenable to a mathematical analysis using a simple, but realistic model. The problem is to describe the rate of movement of a concentration zone through a partition or adsorption column in terms of operating variables. Variables of interest are column geometry and material, column temperature, and the type of carrier gas and its flow rate. These should explicitly define the retention time. The technique will be to view the movement of a concentration zone as a rate process. Since every rate process has an activation energy, the model will predict an activation energy. It will also be shown that this "mechanical" or "kinetic" approach yields an activation energy which permits insight into the mechanism of chromatography.

Kinetic Approach. For gas-solid chromatography we assume an array of adsorption sites within the column with a moving concentration zone consisting of adsorbed gas always in the same dynamic equilibrium with gas in the vapor phase. Gas molecules cannot move when adsorbed, but only when in the vapor phase, and do not lag behind the carrier gas which is not adsorbed. When a zone is in dynamic equilibrium between a gas and solid phase, it can easily be shown that the fraction of time spent by each zone molecule in the gas phase is given by the expression:

$$\frac{n_g}{n_g + n_a} \qquad (4\text{-}1)$$

where n_g = moles of zone in gas phase, and
       n_a = moles of zone adsorbed

Thus, $$u = u_g \frac{n_g}{n_g + n_a} \qquad (4\text{-}2)$$

where u = linear velocity of concentration zone, and
       u_g = linear velocity of carrier gas

which is seen to have the correct boundary conditions. The model states simply that at any instant a zone molecule is either on the surface or in the gas phase. It may move with the carrier only when in the latter phase and its halting journey through the column may be described by an average linear velocity.

The equilibrium constant for adsorption is:

$$H_a \;=\; \frac{\underline{n}a}{\underline{n}g} \tag{4-3}$$

and substituting into equation 4-2, we have:

$$\underline{u} \;=\; \underline{u}_g \; \frac{1}{H_a + 1} \tag{4-4}$$

since $\qquad \underline{u} \;=\; \dfrac{1}{\underline{t}_R}$ and $\underline{u}_g \;=\; \dfrac{F_c}{\underline{a}}$

we substitute these values in equation 4-4, and obtain:

$$\underline{t}_R \;=\; \frac{1\underline{a}}{F_c} \; (1 + H_a) \tag{4-5}$$

where $\underline{1}$ $=$ packed length of adsorption column
$\quad\;\; \underline{t}_R$ $=$ retention time of zone
$\quad\;\; \underline{a}$ $=$ interstitial area of column
$\quad\;\; F_c$ $=$ flow rate of carrier gas

Since the interstitial volume of the column, $V_G^{\,o}$, is equal to $\underline{1a}$, equation 4-5 becomes:

$$\underline{t}_R \;=\; \frac{V_G^{\,o}}{F_c} \; (1 + H_a) \tag{4-6}$$

For parameters usually encountered in equation 4-6, H_a is much larger than unity and

$$\underline{t}_R \;=\; \frac{1\underline{a} \; H_a}{F_c} \tag{4-7}$$

Utilizing the temperature dependence of H_a

$$B \; \exp\left(- \; \frac{Q_a}{RT}\right) \tag{4-8}$$

and substituting in equation 4-7, we have

$$\underline{t}_R = \frac{\underline{l}aB}{F_c} \exp\left(-\frac{Q_a}{RT}\right) \qquad (4-9)$$

where B = a constant

Q_a = heat of adsorption of zone on adsorbent

An analogous treatment of gas-liquid chromatography results in an expression similar to equation 4-6:

$$\underline{t}_R = \frac{V_G^o}{F_c}\left(1 + \frac{HV_L}{V_G^o}\right) \qquad (4-10)$$

or

$$V_R^o = V_G^o + HV_L \qquad (4-11)$$

where $V_R^o = F_c \underline{t}_R$ = limiting retention volume

$V_G^o = \underline{l}a$ = volume of gas phase in column

V_L = volume of liquid phase in column

H = partition coefficient, ratio of concentration of solute in liquid and gas phase

From equation 4-8, we derive:

$$\underline{t}_R = \frac{\underline{l}a}{F_c}\left[1 + C \exp\left(-\frac{Q_s}{RT}\right)\right] \qquad (4-12)$$

where Q_s is the heat of solution of the eluted gas in the liquid phase. If solutions are ideal, Q_s may be replaced by Q_v, where the latter is the heat of vaporization of the gas.

From equations 4-9 and 4-12 it is seen that retention time is inversely proportional to carrier gas flow rate, directly proportional to column length and exponentially proportional to temperature. The variation of retention time in this fashion has been shown by various authors (323, 582) for both gas-solid chromatography and gas-liquid chromatography.

From equation 4-10 it can be deduced that the re-

tention time is made up of two terms; the amount of time a
gas molecule spends in the gas phase, V_G^o/F_c , and the
amount of time in the liquid phase, HV_L/F_c . Note that both
equations 4-6 and 4-10 are general equations, saying nothing of the carrier or eluted gas, and that only the partition
or adsorption coefficient is responsible for separation of
gases. Furthermore, in eluting a series of gases from a
single column, the amount of time spent in the gas phase is
identical for all gases, but the amount of time in the liquid
or solid phases is variable.

Determination of Heat of Adsorption or Solution.
From equations 4-9 and 4-12 it can be seen that a plot of ln
retention time corrected for the amount of time in the gas
phase versus $1/T$ should yield the heat of adsorption of an
eluted gas on the column packing for adsorption columns and
the heat of solution (vaporization if ideal solutions are formed) in the liquid of partition columns. The latter plot must,
of course, be corrected for the coefficient of expansion of
the liquid phase. The heats have been derived and shown to
agree quite well with those obtained by independent methods.
Heats derived for n-butane from the slope of the straight
line plot of ln t_R versus $1/T$ are shown in Table 4-1 (582).

TABLE 4-1.   HEATS OF n-BUTANE DERIVED FROM
TEMPERATURE COEFFICIENTS OF
RETENTION TIMES

Column Material	Heat (Cal/mole)
Activated alumina	8700
Di-n-ocytl phthalate (on Celite)	5360
Triisobutylene (on Celite)	5530

The derived heat of adsorption would seem to be reasonable for coverages at or less than one monolayer. The heat of adsorption of n-butane or alumina at $0^{\circ}C$ has been determined from BET parameters as 8200 cal/mole (323). The heat of solution derived from the partition columns is in fair agreement with the heat of vaporization of n-butane. The heat of vaporization at the average temperature of the experiment was 5100 cal/mole (421).

Since the activation energy of the chromatographic process is associated with zone molecules entering and leaving the liquid, apparently diffusion can play only a second order role.

Partition or activity coefficients have been determined utilizing equation 4-9 (110, 292, 636) and agree well with partition coefficients derived directly from equilibrium methods. Note also from equations 4-5 and 4-8 that the retention volume is independent of flow rate.

Since the activation energy of the chromatographic process is apparently associated with zone molecules entering or leaving the surface for both gas-solid and gas-liquid chromatography, diffusion in the liquid phase is expected to play only a second order role. Diffusion controlled processes are proportional to the square root of the absolute temperature and the retention time would have been essentially insensitive to temperature over the relatively small temperature range utilized in the experiments illustrated in Table 4-1.

EFFECT OF CARRIER GAS ON RETENTION TIME

From equations 4-9 and 4-12, it can be seen that carrier gases might play a relatively minor role in influencing separations. Their only contribution could be to affect either the heat of solution or adsorption of the concentration zone and thus the retention time. The effect may be appreciable since the dependence is exponential.

Effect with Partition Columns. For gas-liquid chromatography the more cryogenic carrier gases such as helium, hydrogen, argon, or nitrogen will be negligibly soluble in the liquid phase and will thus not effect the heat of solution. Use of such gases as acetylene, propane, or

butane are expected to exhibit solubility in organic phases,
but such experiments would be academic, since it is simpler
to modify heats of solution by addition of other liquids to the
partitioning phase.

Effect with Adsorption Columns. For gas-solid
chromatography carrier gases can theoretically have a pronounced effect on retention time. Charcoal, a common adsorbent, can adsorb at room temperature appreciable quantities of typically used carrier gases such as nitrogen, argon, and carbon dioxide. We postulate a fixed number of
adsorption sites, admit the possibility of carrier gases com-
peting for the sites, and question the effect on retention time.
Qualitatively, if carrier gas is adsorbed, one would expect
the retention time to be reduced. A simple argument would
suggest that if adsorption sites can also be occupied by adsorbed carrier gas then the total amount of time a zone molecule spends at a given site can only be reduced. Thus, the
effective length of the column is reduced as is the retention
time as predicted by equation 4-5. If a series of carrier
gases which were adsorbed in increasing amounts, were
used to elute a gas, then the retention time of the eluted gas
would be reduced increasingly. The phenomenon has been
verified (405) and is illustrated in Table 4-2. Heats of adsorption obtained with carriers which are adsorbed are
shown in Table 4-3. It is seen that the derived heat of adsorption is decreased, the decrease caused being greater
for those carriers which would be expected to be adsorbed
to the greatest extent. Equation 4-9 predicts the decrease
in retention time as the derived heat of adsorption is lowered. In spite of these experiments, the factors causing decreased retention time are not completely understood. It is
possible for the retention time to be reduced while the heat
of adsorption is unaffected as in the case of a homogeneous
surface in the absence of adsorbate interactions.

From Table 4-4 it can be seen that in the case of
ethylene and acetylene, the derived heats of adsorption are
comparable to heats of vaporization. Thus, adsorbed carrier gases have completely destroyed the adsorption properties of the adsorbent and what corresponds to a gas-liquid
partition column results. Adsorbed carrier gas is pictured
to be deposited on the adsorbent surface as a liquid-like film.

TABLE 4-2. EFFECT OF CARRIER GAS ON RETENTION
TIMES OF METHANE

Carrier Gas	Retention Time, min*
Helium	34
Argon	22
Air	15
Nitrogen	16
Acetylene	5

*Retention times of methane on a 10-ft charcoal column
at 25°C, flow rate of carrier gases is 70 cc/min.

Further exploitation of this technique is expected
to increase the power of gas chromatography. Carrier gases
such as hydrogen chloride, hydrogen sulfide, or hydrogen
cyanide could be utilized to deposit liquid-like films on adsorbents for specific separations.

Since the adsorption of carrier gas reduces the retention time of eluted gases, the time between eluted peaks
will be less and separations in general, less clean. Janak
(68) used carbon dioxide as a carrier gas and adsorbed the
effluent in potassium hydroxide, volumetrically recording
the eluted gases. If one reviews his separations on both
silica gel and alumina and compares them with those of
Greene and Pust (403) obtained by using helium, one is immediately impressed by the effect of carrier gas adsorption
on separation efficiency. This is especially evident with
alumina, since the adsorbent irreversibly adsorbs carbon
dioxide.

SELECTION OF CARRIER GAS

Detector Considerations. Gas chromatographic
instruments usually employ thermal conductivity cell detectors, either of the hot wire or thermistor type. Thus, the
larger the difference between the thermal conductivity of
carrier and eluted gas, the larger is the signal. The kinetic

theory of gases states that the thermal conductivity of a gas is inversely proportional to the square root of the molecular weight. The two lightest gases, hydrogen and helium, are excellent candidates for carrier gases since they are readily available in pressurized cylinders, inexpensive, and farthest removed in thermal conductivity from other gases. Table 4-5 lists the thermal conductivities of various gases of interest.

TABLE 4-3. EFFECT OF CARRIER GAS ON DERIVED HEATS (Kcal/mole)

A.   ALUMINA
Carrier Gas

	He	C_2H_2	C_2H_4
C_3H_8	7150	3320	4000
C_4H_{10}	8700	3400	——

B.   SILICA GEL
Carrier Gas

	He	C_2H_2
CO_2	6290	2400
C_3H_8	8060	3230

C.   CHARCOAL
Carrier Gas

	He	N_2	Ar	CH_4
CH_4	4840	4100	3500	——
CO	3350	3000	2500	2000

TABLE 4-4. COMPARISON OF DERIVED HEATS OF ADSORPTION AND HEATS OF VAPORIZATION

GAS	CARRIER	HEAT (cal/mole)	ΔH_v* (cal/mole)
C_3H_8	C_2H_2	3230	3640
CO_2	C_2H_2	2400	2090
C_3H_8	C_2H_2	3320	3640
C_3H_8	C_2H_4	4000	3640

*Ref. 421.

Hydrogen, helium, and nitrogen offer adequate sensitivity for analysis of all organic vapors. For analysis of inorganic gases, oxygen, argon, and neon in addition to those already mentioned.

Sample column material and detector elements should be inert to the carrier gas. Glycol-silver nitrate columns used to separate ethylene and ethane (110) are rapidly reduced by hydrogen at room temperature. Carrier gases which are expected to have a deleterious effect on filaments should not be used, or if necessary, the operating temperature of the filaments reduced.

Hydrogen gas would be expected to hydrogenate carbon dioxide, oxygen and unsaturated hydrocarbons at the surface of hot wire filaments. An explosion hazard is possible with the use of hydrogen, and the column effluent should be properly vented.

Cost of Gas. The cost of carrier gases is usually low and has a minor consideration. An expensive carrier gas, such as neon, is used for some special separations. Operating costs at 20 ml/min. flow are $12 per hour for carrier gas alone.

Effect on Sensitivity. There are instances where the similarity between thermal conductivity of carrier and an eluted gas reduces the sensitivity to such an extent that the analysis is not reliable. Complications arise when attempting to analyze hydrogen using the more standard carrier gas helium. The thermal conductivities are so similar that little sensitivity results and the analysis cannot be made with precision. Table 4-6 lists the response of various gases to candidate carriers. Those marked with an asterisk show adequate sensitivity for quantitative analysis.

TABLE 4-5. THERMAL CONDUCTIVITIES OF VARIOUS GASES AT 0 °C

Gas	Thermal conductivity[*] Cal./cm. sec. °C x 10^5
Hydrogen	39.60
Helium	33.60
Nitrogen	5.68
Oxygen	5.70
Carbon Dioxide	3.393
Carbon Monoxide	5.425
Isopentane	2.912
Argon	3.88
Neon	10.4
Nitric Oxide	5.55

*Lange, N.A., HANDBOOK OF CHEMISTRY, (1949)

TABLE 4-6. SENSITIVITY OF GASES TO VARIOUS
CARRIERS.

	H_2	He	Ar	N_2	Ne
H_2			*	*	**
He			*	*	**
CO	*	*	*		*
CO_2	*	*	a	**	*
O_2	*	*	*		*
NO	*	*	*		*
N_2	*	*	*		*
Ar	*	*		*	*
HC	*	*	*	*	*

HC - Hydrocarbons
 *   - Adequate sensitivity for quantitative analysis
 ** - Signal will be negative as compared to other gases
 a   - Sensitivity depends markedly on filament current

Effect on Separation. Probably the most troublesome gas mixtures to analyze are those from flames, which
include hydrogen, oxides of carbon, nitrogen, and some hydrocarbons. In order to avoid duplicate runs with different
carrier gases, neon might be utilized. Although the gas is
expensive ($1.00/liter), the advantages have been found to
outweigh the price. There are some special separations for
which only neon is adequate. For example, it was desired
to separate small concentrations H_2, HD, and D_2 in helium
(700). Obviously helium could not be utilized as the carrier
since there would not have been adequate sensitivity. For
any separation at all, the temperature of the separation
would need to be reduced considerably, using a charcoal

column immersed in liquid oxygen. Carrier gases such as
nitrogen and argon were utilized, but no separations were
obtained. It was theorized that the carriers were adsorbed
to the extent that a liquid-like film formed on the charcoal
surface, and in effect a partition column resulted. The
same separations were attempted with neon carrier gas with
partially successful results. Helium, hydrogen (both ortho
and para) were well separated, but HD could not be completely separated from D_2. The separations were attempted at
liquid nitrogen temperatures, and with silica gel and alumina,
with essentially the same results.

The separation of hydrogen and helium can be accomplished on charcoal at room temperature on twenty foot
charcoal columns utilizing either argon or nitrogen as the
carrier gas. The wave form of hydrogen is interesting in
that it has a leading front and sharp back. With argon or
nitrogen one must utilize long columns, or reduce the temperature of shorter ones to $0^{\circ}C$ in order to separate cleanly
hydrogen and nitrogen. Use of neon produces a completely
symmetrical hydrogen peak form and hydrogen and helium
are separated at room temperature in short columns.

The separation of argon and oxygen has not been
reported on any of the more common adsorbents. Greene
(700) has utilized oxygen carrier to blank out the oxygen contained in argon-oxygen mixtures and the oxygen was determined by difference.

It is interesting that elution of small samples of
hydrogen with helium results in a signal where polarity indicates that hydrogen has a thermal conductivity less than
that of helium. As the sample size is continuously increased,
a minimum appears in the wave form which ultimately becomes negative with respect to the baseline (616). The total
signal is then composed of two positive peaks and a negative
one. The same effect has been observed utilizing oxygen as
the carrier with large samples of nitrogen (700) and is apparently associated with similarity in the thermal conductivity of carrier and eluted gas.

CARRIER GAS FLOW RATE

Control of carrier gas flow rate is easily accomplished by control of a pressure drop almost anywhere in

the flow circuit. Commercially available pressure regulators such as those manufactured by the Conoflow Corporation or the Fischer and Porter Company are adequate for setting a constant pressure to the head of the column.

Control Requirements. Various investigators report the effects of carrier gas flow rate on detector response. Percival (475) says that column flow rate must be controlled to 0.2% in order to keep the error in analyses belòw 0.5%. Similar results are reported by Dimbat and co-workers (198), who claimed that flow rate must be controlled to 1% in order to reduce the analytical error below 1%. Both detectors are typical of those used in gas chromatography and the results are probably representative. The simplest and least expensive instrument from which one can determine pressure changes (and hence flow rates) of 0.5-1% is the differential manometer, preferably reading a differential at least 200 mm. When carrier gas flow rates are measured by a pressure drop at the column exit using a differential manometer, the elution of a peak will cause a pressure surge in the manometer due to the change in viscosity of gas flowing through the restricting orifice. The phenomenon could possibly be utilized as a method of detection.

Effect of Flow Rate on Peak Height, Area, and Shape. Retention time is used to identify components emerging from columns. Therefore, it is essential that flow rate be known or constant. For quantitative analysis the flow rate should be precisely controlled because of the effect on detector signals. If carrier gas is permitted to pass over the filaments at varying rates, then the amount of heat removed by the carrier from the filament will be variable, as will be filament temperature, response and sensitivity. There are, however, cell geometries which minimize the effects of fluctuations in flow, but the effect is a spurious one and not amenable to mathematical treatment.

Flow rate has a definite intrinsic effect on peak area which may be predicted from simple mechanical considerations. Consider a recorder which amplifies the detector cell output and has a constant chart speed. The filaments are in the directed path of the carrier flow. The sensitivity is linear and independent of flow, and the response

is measured at a given flow for a given amount of eluted gas.
We define the response, or peak area, as

$$r = g\ m\ s\ C_1\ C_2/C_3$$

where r =   response = peak area, mv x min
         g =   proportionality constant
         s =   detector sensitivity, mv/weight of solute, a
                  constant
         m =   weight of solute introduced to column
         C_1 = chart speed, cm/min
         C_2 = detector amplification factor
         C_3 = carrier gas flow rate, ml/min

The detector sensitivity is assumed to be a constant and depends only on the thermal conductivity of carrier
and solute, and the properties of the filaments. We repeat
the experiment with the same amount of solute but at twice
the carrier gas flow rate and note the effects on peak height,
peak width at the base line, and peak area. The peak height
was found to remain constant while the area was halved utilizing gas-liquid partition techniques (198), suggesting the
base line to be halved when a triangular approximation to
the peak form is assumed. Percival (475) found the product
of the peak area and flow rate to be relatively insensitive to
flow utilizing gas adsorption techniques.

One might expect this inverse relationship between
carrier flow (linear velocity) and peak area. When the carrier gas flow rate is doubled, its linear velocity is approximately doubled and the detector responds to the identical
varying concentrations of solute on a time scale that is con-
densed by a factor of one-half. The peak height observed in
the second experiment would not be expected to change,
since carrier gas flow has theoretically no effect on the partition coefficient or the partial pressure of an eluted gas.

Effect of Carrier Gas Flow Rate on Separation.
From equation 4-5 it is seen that the retention time is inversely proportional to the carrier gas flow rate. The components of a gas mixture travel through a given column at a
given carrier gas flow at velocities which are a function
only of their partition coefficients. It is obvious that a

longer column at constant carrier gas velocity, or a slower
carrier gas velocity at constant column length, will result
in a better separation of the components. It is the relative
linear velocities of zones in columns which ultimately permits their separation. Thus, if the ratio of retention volumes of two gases are determined at a given flow rate, theoretically the ratio will be the same at any other flow rate,
greater or smaller. However, the separation as determined
qualitatively by the distance between zone peaks, will be different. The idea is illustrated in Table 4-7 where theory
indicates that separation improves with decreasing carrier
flow rate on a given column.

TABLE 4-7. THEORETICAL VARIATION OF RETENTION TIME AND SEPARATION OF TWO GASES WITH CARRIER FLOW RATE

Flow Rate	1000	200	100	50	10
t_R(Gas A)	0.2	1	2	4	20
t_R(Gas B)	0.5	2.5	5	10	50
Separation*	0.3	1.5	3	6	30

*t_R gas B - t_R gas A

        In reality, one cannot continually decrease the car-
rier gas flow rate in order to improve the separation of two
gases. Aside from lengthening analysis time, there exists
a region of diminishing return in decreasing flow rate. The
retention time is inversely proportional to flow rate, and
although the peak positions are pushed farther apart by decreasing flow, diffusional peak spreading may become so
severe that separation is in reality not improved in return.
        The resolving power limit is attained when condi-
tions are such that increased retention time broadens two
adjacent peaks at the same rate as their peaks are separated. When this happens a different or modified partition

liquid must be used in order to improve separation.

Separation Efficiency and Carrier Gas Flow Rate.

The concept of the number of theoretical plates in a liquid chromatographic column was developed by Martin and Synge (5) and may be directly applied to gas chromatography. Qualitatively the concept is simply a measure of the amount of zone spreading during transit through a chromatographic column. We must be cautious in defining efficiency (plates) and resolution. The former is theoretically capable of exact mathematical computation, and is an indication of zone spreading, not separation, as in an ordinary distillation column. The latter term refers to the degree of separation of gases. We can have chromatographic columns with an enormous number of plates, while the resolution of some gases is quite poor. As described in Chapter 2, the number of theoretical plates in a gas chromatographic column is determined from the expression: $\underline{n} = 16\,(\underline{t}_R/\,\Delta\underline{t})$. The expression is derived from chromatographic theories which predict the shape of an eluted zone and picture the separation process to be analogous with that in a distillation column. Mass transfer rates are infinite, diffusion is neglected, and band broadening is proportional to the square root of the number of theoretical plates. The mechanisms of band broadening are not contained within the theories. Both $\underline{t}_R$ and $\Delta\underline{t}$ are inversely proportional to flow rate, and the number of theoretical plates should be independent of flow rate.

The more elaborate theory of gas chromatography developed by van Deemter et al.(316) takes into account mass transfer and diffusion, and results in an expression which shows the dependence of HETP on carrier gas flow rate. The familiar van Deemter equation indicates the HETP to consist of three contributions, and may be written in the following simplified form: $\text{HETP} = A + B/\underline{u} + C\underline{u}$.

The phenomenon of band broadening, that is, HETP, will be minimum at a certain carrier gas flow rate and at that flow rate, the separation efficiency will be greatest. The effect of carrier gas flow rate on the separation of o- and p- xylene (276) is illustrated in Fig. 4-1.

Hydrogen and helium stand apart in their low molecular weights and hence high diffusivities. Gases diffuse

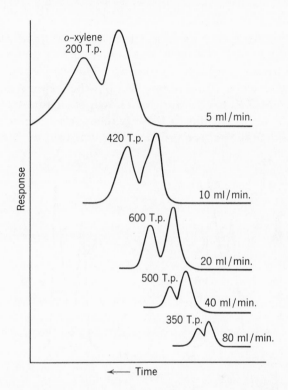

Fig. 4-1. Separation of o- and p-xylene. After Mellor (276).

3-4 times as rapidly through hydrogen than through nitrogen. Peak broadening caused by diffusion in hydrogen would be expected to be more pronounced than in nitrogen and the latter would be the preferred carrier gas provided sensitivity was adequate. It has been found (171) that clean separations of propane and propylene could be obtained with nitrogen carrier while hydrogen produced severe overlapping. The separations are illustrated in Fig. 4-2.

Retention Time and Pressure-Flow Relations. Since there is a pressure drop across gas chromatographic column, the carrier gas as well as the eluted zone will undergo an acceleration as they pass through the column.

In order to determine heats of solution and partition coefficients, and to standardize retention volumes determined experimentally, it is necessary to deduce a reten-

tion volume that is independent of the pressure change along
the column. The retention volume obtained by multiplication
of retention time and carrier flow as measured at the column exit is a true constant only when there is a negligible
pressure drop across the column. The concept is illustrated
in Table 4-8 where the term, $F_c t_R$, the experimentally determined retention volume, is shown as a function of pressure ratio or its adjunct, flow rate across the column. It
is assumed that the pressure at the column exit will be one

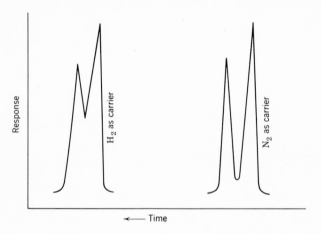

Fig. 4-2.   Separation of propane and propylene with 30%
            triisobutylene on Celite. After Bosanquet and
            Morgan (171).

TABLE 4-8.   EFFECT OF PRESSURE RATIO ON
             OBSERVED RETENTION VOLUME

P_i/P_o	$F_c t_R$
1.00	1.00
1.02	1.01
1.05	1.03
1.10	1.05
1.50	1.27
2.0	1.56
3.0	2.16
4.0	4.2

atmosphere and 25°C. The complication arises simply because gases are compressible and will be resolved by computing the limiting retention volume V_R^o, which is the retention volume which would have been observed at zero pressure drop across the column.

The correction factor for pressure drop across the column has been derived by James and Martin (44, 47). The average pressure in the column is given by:

$$\bar{p} = \frac{2}{3} \, p_o \, \frac{(p_i/p_o)^3 - 1}{(p_i/p_o)^2 - 1}$$

and the limiting, or corrected, retention volume is given by

$$V_R^o = V_R \, \frac{3}{2} \, \frac{(p_i/p_o)^2 - 1}{(p_i/p_o)^3 - 1}$$

and
$$V_R^o \, / \, V_R = p_o/\bar{p} \; .$$

Chapter 5

STATIONARY PHASE

H. S. Knight

Shell Development Company

THE CHARACTERISTICS OF ADSORBENTS for use in GSC are very similar to those for liquid phase chromatography, and include adequate surface area, reasonable particle size and chemical inertness. Many established liquid phase adsorbents have simply been taken over for GSC.

ADSORBENTS FOR GAS-SOLID CHROMATOGRAPHY

Activated Carbon. Madison (616) used activated carbon to separate the fixed gases, hydrogen, oxygen, nitrogen, carbon monoxide and methane (Fig. 5-1). His col-

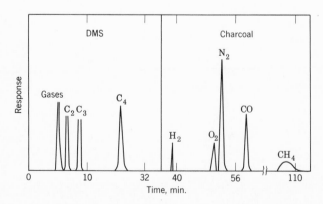

Fig. 5-1. Two-stage separation of gases and light hydro-carbons. Courtesy of Analytical Chemistry (616).

48

umn was 25 ft. long and was operated at 20°C. His work is of special interest because he used a two-column technique with only one thermal conductivity detector and recorder. A liquid partition column separated the above gases from ethane and propane, and the gases were trapped in a short column of activated carbon maintained at liquid nitrogen temperature. The trap was disconnected while the ethane and propane emerged. Then the trap, the long carbon column and the detector were connected, and the carrier passed through the assembly while the trap was warmed. The gases were released to be separated by the carbon column.

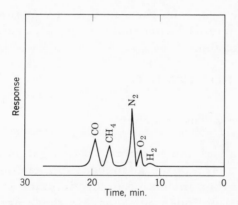

Fig. 5-2. Separation of gases on Molecular Sieve 5A. Courtesy of American Chemical Society (362).

Madison observed positive peaks for hydrogen in small amounts, but negative peaks with positive front and back sections for large amounts of hydrogen. The reasons for this were discussed in Chapter 4.

Molecular Sieve. Davis and Schreiber (362) developed a more elaborate two-column separation using two detectors and recorders. Their GLC column will be described later. They used Molecular Sieve 5A for the gas analysis portion. Their column was 15 ft. long and was held at 100°C (Fig. 5-2). Note that the gases emerged in 20 min as opposed to 60 min on activated carbon, and that methane was ahead of carbon monoxide. Carbon dioxide was determined by these workers on their partition column.

Greene (583) also used Molecular Sieve 5A for gas analysis. He deliberately violated the rule about chemical inertness of the support to determine nitrogen dioxide. This gas does not emerge from an ordinary GSC column and tails badly in GLC. Greene added two ml of water to the inlet end of the Molecular Sieve column to bring about these reactions:

$$2\ NO_2 + H_2O \rightarrow HNO_2 + HNO_3$$

$$3\ HNO_2 \rightarrow HNO_3 + 2\ NO + H_2O$$

The nitric oxide peak was then used as a measure of the nitrogen dioxide originally present. After correcting for the equilibrium reaction:

$$2\ NO_2 \rightleftharpoons N_2O_4$$

the results were about as expected.

Silica Gel and Alumina. Silica gel was employed by Smith et al. (642) as the adsorbent in a chemically-aided separation of carbon monoxide or nitric oxide from nitrogen. Ordinarily silica gel does not separate these gases. A short section in the middle of the column was packed with iodine pentoxide followed by silver metal to react with any iodine released. If carbon monoxide was present it was converted to carbon dioxide in the middle of the column. The entire column separated the carbon dioxide in the original sample, and the second half separated the carbon dioxide representing the original carbon monoxide to half as great an extent.

In the case of nitrous oxide the oxidation product was nitrogen dioxide which failed to emerge from the dry column. The amount of nitrous oxide was determined by difference, by comparing a similar analysis without the oxidant in the column.

Patton et al. (151) separated low boiling hydrocarbons through C_5 by GSC and employed calibration factors to convert peak heights to concentrations. Fig. 5-3 shows that the later peaks tended to be distorted more and more. Such distortions usually restrict GSC to light gases.

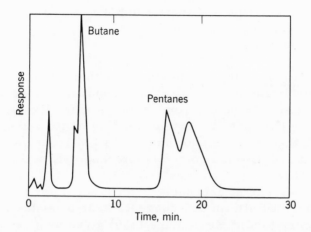

Fig. 5-3. GSC separation of hydrocarbons. Courtesy of
Analytical Chemistry (151).

Greene and Pust (403) were able to work with fixed
gases and up to C_4 by operating the 20 ft. silica or alumina
column at a continuously increasing temperature. The fixed
gases began emerging at $5^{\circ}C$ and the butanes were complet-
ed at $150^{\circ}C$ an hour later. The volatility of the material represented by the tail was raised by the higher temperature,
reducing the tail. As a matter of fact, their somewhat styl-
ized curves indicate that tailing under these conditions was
negligible. The rising temperature technique will be discussed further in Chapters 7 and 11.

PHYSICAL CHARACTERISTICS OF THE STATIONARY PHASE IN GAS-LIQUID CHROMATOGRAPHY

Solid Support. When used as a support for a liquid,
the solid material in the column should have large intercon-
nected pores which provide minimum hindrance to diffusion.
Such materials have low surface area, perhaps less than
20 m^2/g. Like the adsorbents, the supports should have
reasonable particle size and chemical inertness. Diatoma-
ceous earths such as Celite, and their derived products
such as crushed insulating brick, are almost universally
used. As one exception, Ellis and Iveson (569) used Teflon
or Kel-F particles impregnated with liquid poly(trifluoro-

monochloroethylene) as a solvent for analyzing blends of chlorine and fluorine and their compounds. Various workers have used a commercial detergent as a combination support and liquid phase.

Liquid Phase. The solvents themselves are normally nonvolatile, chemically inert liquids. As the temperature is raised decomposition becomes more likely, and the solvent itself is lost at a rate depending on its vapor pressure. Whitham (556) found that DC-710 silicone gave off benzene at 250°C when coated on Sterchamol, a European insulating brick.

As a first approach to setting a vapor pressure limit, Burrell Bulletin 835 suggests 0.01 or at the most 0.1 mm mercury (352). Keulemans (439) gives proposed maximum operating temperatures for various solvents. Table 5-1 contains some of the available suggested limits from these and other sources.

TABLE 5-1. SUGGESTED MAXIMUM TEMPERATURES
FOR VARIOUS GLC SOLVENTS, °C.

Dimethylformamide	20
Dimethylsulfolane	25
Diglycerol	100
Polyglycols	100
Carbowax 1000	180
Dinonyl phthalate	140
Squalane	140
DC-710 silicone	250
Bitumen	250
Apiezon L	250
Asphaltenes	320
High Vacuum Silicone Grease	350

A little familiarity with these solvents shows that none suitable for operation at 200°C or higher is polar, when compared with diglycerol or dimethylformamide. Since high boiling samples are also relatively nonpolar, solvent effects tend to be weak where they are most needed because of the multiplicity of isomers.

The result is a tendency to stretch the ideal limits

a little. What happens then? In the first place some solvent will be lost. More will probably be lost from high solvent concentration columns than from low, because volatility of thin films is reduced somewhat by adsorption. If the vapor pressure is 1 mm the loss will be some 0.1 gram per day from a 1/4 in. column. Most of this will come from the first part of the column, where the support may become dry. Dry supports affect peak times and shapes (Chapter 7). In the less extreme case the retention volumes will be reduced, but the relative times will not be changed. Taylor and Dunlop (505) used a dimethylformamide column until it became noticeably worse from the standpoint of separation efficiency before replacing it (Fig. 5-4). They disregarded small changes in absolute times which did not affect the analysis.

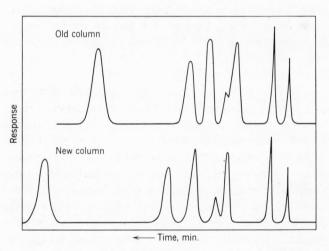

Fig. 5-4. Separation of hydrocarbons on old and new columns. Courtesy of Instrument Society of America (551).

To a large extent, the solvent level on the column can be maintained by saturating the carrier at column temperature before it enters the apparatus. By this technique Kwantes and Rijnders (606) were able to pass a compound over a solvent consisting of the next higher member of the same homologous series. This work was discussed in Chapter 3.

Another problem with volatile solvents is condensation in cooler parts of the apparatus. A droplet of solvent

bubbling in a restriction will change the carrier flow, and
wreak havoc with an otherwise suitable baseline. If the detector is non-flow-sensitive, a solvent droplet in the cell
chamber may still affect the response. Such condensation
will surely occur in the trap used to collect samples, and
affect any further analysis.

Finally, the amount of solvent in the carrier will
vary with column temperature, causing baseline drift (long
term change) or even noise (short term change) if the temperature control is poor.

The problem of solvent evaporation is most severe with industrial apparatus designed to read out in the
form of a bar graph, where each peak is timed. Any change
in column characteristics can force frequent readjustment
of the controls.

There are two entirely different stationary phases
not touched on before. One is the capillary tubing wetted-
wall column of Golay (395, 577) where the inside of the tube
serves as the support.

Combustors. The other type of "stationary phase"
is a hot copper oxide bed used to oxidize the sample, as discussed for example by Norem (468). Some advantages of
oxidizing the sample are as follows. The detector can be
operated at low temperature, particularly if the water is
removed on a drying column, as is usually the case. Maximum sensitivity can be achieved with katharometer detectors, because the temperature difference between the sensing element and the carrier can be a maximum. Then too,
carbon dioxide derived from a hydrocarbon weighs more than
the hydrocarbon, and thermal conductivity detectors are
sensitive to weight. Finally, the recorded curve will be entirely on a carbon dioxide basis, so no calibration factors
will be needed to correct the areas for varying detector response to different materials.

Disadvantages are that the components must be
known in order to calculate the results. For example, methyl alcohol will appear as one carbon but ethane will appear
as two, and so on. Identification of the components by trapping is impossible without equipment alterations. Difficulties with less common elements can be envisioned, such as
poisoning the oxidant and complicating the area interpreta-

tion. Without the oxidation step no calibration factors need be used as a first approximation, with helium or hydrogen carrier. The added equipment undoubtedly reduces the efficiency somewhat by adding to opportunities for diffusion.

Chapter 6

COLUMN

CONDITIONS

H. S. Knight

Shell Development Company

EFFECT ON EFFICIENCY

EFFICIENCY MEANS the ability of the column to produce
narrow peaks, which will be adequately resolved even though
the peak maxima are not separated very far in time. Efficiency is measured in theoretical plates, where one plate
corresponds to one equilibrium stage in a stepwise separation. An equation for calculating plates from a GLC curve
is as follows:

$$\text{No. of plates} = \underline{n} = \left(\frac{4\,V_R}{\Delta V}\right)^2$$

where V_R is the retention volume measured from the time
of charging the sample and ΔV is the extrapolated peak
width in volume units. Both may be measured in distance
on the chart. (Compare with equation 2-1). Actually separation is a continuous process and plates are just a mathematical convenience, already familiar to many through the
analogy with packed columns in distillation.

Van Deemter Equation. An equation for predict-
ing efficiency, derived from considerations of GLC as a
continuous process, is due to van Deemter et al. (316).
This equation gathers the important variables contributing

to efficiency together and shows the approximate effect of
each. Some supporting data have been given by De Wet and
Pretorius (559) and some contrary data are discussed later.
The equation yields HETP, the height equivalent to a theoretical plate, or the length of column corresponding to one
equilibrium stage. It is usually expressed in centimeters.

$$HETP = 2\lambda \underline{d_p} + 2\frac{\gamma D_{gas}}{\underline{u}} + \frac{8 \underline{k'}}{\pi^2(1+\underline{k'})^2} \cdot \frac{d_f^2}{D_{liq}} \underline{u}$$

This is often reduced for discussion purposes to:

$$HETP = A + B/\underline{u} + C\underline{u}$$

The effects of operating conditions on HETP have
already been mentioned in Chapter 2, and will be reviewed
here. We will discuss the equation in terms of A, B, and C,
referring back to the original for the makeup of these constants.

The A term is made up of two factors, λ and $\underline{d_p}$,
representing packing irregularity and particle diameter. A
large packing irregularity and a small particle diameter
counterbalance. For example, unsized Celite particles are
very small but columns made from them are not as efficient
as those made from coarser grades. It is considered that
the fine particles do not pack well enough. The A term is
independent of linear velocity, $\underline{u}$.

The $B/\underline{u}$ term disappears at high velocity. The
diffusion in the gas phase, D_{gas}, is reduced owing to lack
of time. The $\overline{\gamma}$ is the packing tortuosity factor.

The $C\underline{u}$ term becomes larger at higher velocity.
It represents the degree of equilibrium attainment during
the separation. $\underline{k'}$ is a measure of the ratio of solute in the
liquid to solute in the gas phase. Good solvents result in
high values for $\underline{k'}$ giving better efficiency. The film depth,
$\underline{d_f}$, appears as the square. D_{liq} is the diffusion in the liquid
phase. At high velocity this will limit equilibrium attain-
ment.

The effect of temperature on efficiency is not explicitly covered by the van Deemter equation, but temperature enters in through the diffusion terms and $\underline{k'}$. As temperature increases, D_{gas} and D_{liq} increase, having opposite

effects on HETP. The value of $\underline{k}'$ will decrease as more
solute will be forced into the gas phase, decreasing the efficiency. The net effect will depend on the magnitude of all
these changes.

The effect of liquid film depth may be seen by ref-
erence to the $\underline{Cu}$ term. The depth itself occurs as the square,
but thicker films increase the amount of solute in the liquid
phase as represented by $\underline{k}'$, and hence the effect is less
marked than otherwise.

The equation may be plotted as in Fig. 6-1. It is
shown that there is an optimum linear velocity.

The data necessary to calculate HETP from the
equation will in general not be available. All of the practical variables have been studied empirically by various workers, and some of their results will be discussed next.

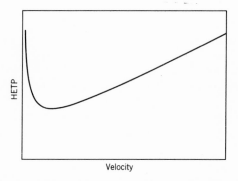

Fig. 6-1. Plot of the van Deemter equation.

Experimental Verification of the van Deemter Equation.

Rangel (296) investigated the effect of temperature using propane solute over kerosine solvent. He concluded that the lower the temperature the better, down to
the freezing point of the solvent. The writer believes that
this will not be true of viscous solvents like glycols, with
which D_{liq} will increase rapidly with increasing temperature.

Cheshire and Scott (549) studied the effect of particle size on column efficiency. They concluded that finer
particles led to higher efficiency, at least up to 120-160
mesh. A wide range fraction, 100-200 mesh, was inferior
to the 100-120 material (Fig. 6-2). They settled on 100-120

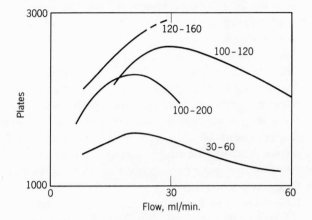

Fig. 6-2. Number of plates as a function of flow rate and particle size. After Cheshire and Scott (549).

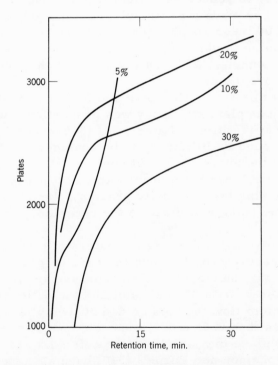

Fig. 6-3. Plate efficiency as affected by solvent concentration and retention time. After Cheshire and Scott (549).

mesh as optimum in glass equipment, as the fine particles produced dangerously high pressures at the optimum flow rate. These workers also studied the effects of the concentration of liquid phase on the support, and of retention time, on efficiency. The results are shown in summary form in Fig. 6-3. The curves rise steeply with increasing retention time, then become linear, except for the 5% solvent case. The highest boiling component of the hydrocarbon test mixture emerged in about 10 min at the low solvent concentration. The curve had not become linear at that time. The authors interpret the general shapes of the curves in terms of the van Deemter equation.

Cheshire and Scott recommended long columns of 5% solvent (5 parts per 100 of support) for low boiling samples. The long column retards them sufficiently for good separation. Shorter columns are recommended for high boiling materials, to reduce analytical time. Based on these principles, they made a 25 ft. column of 5% Apiezon L solvent on 60-100 mesh support (even 100-120 was too fine for this long column in glass equipment) to compare with the above 5 ft. columns. With 0.4 mg samples they obtained 10,000 or more plates.

In this work, Cheshire and Scott claimed that with their conditions plate efficiency was proportional to column length for the first time.. Later Scott (640) made a 50 ft. column and found its efficiency to be considerably less than twice that of the above 25 ft. column. He attributed the discrepancy to the large ratio of inlet to outlet pressure, with its accompanying large velocity gradient. It was impossible to operate the column at close to the optimum velocity throughout.

To reduce the pressure ratio while still providing adequate pressure drop to move the carrier gas, he converted to metal equipment and operated the entire assembly under pressure. With 200 psi inlet and the outlet restricted to give optimum flow the column had 30,000 plates, for an HETP of less than 0.06 cm. He used a special charging technique to place the sample on the column.

Bohemon and Purnell (540) have also studied the effects of particle size on column efficiency. They used a 120 cm column of 20% polyethylene glycol solvent and nitrogen carrier. Their detector consisted of a single thermal conductivity filament. They blended 30-40 and 50-60 mesh crushed brick and obtained worse results until the blend was more than half fine grade. Again, the narrow range support was preferable. With 100-120 mesh support and nitrogen carrier they obtained 1400 plates per ft. for an HETP of 0.05 cm. They found that as sample size was decreased the efficiency increased (Fig. 6-4). The effect was most marked for isopropyl alcohol, less so for hydrocarbons and acetone.

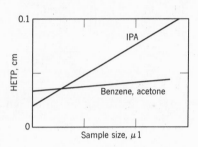

Fig. 6-4. Effect of sample size on column efficiency. After Bohemon and Purnell (540).

In interpreting their results they used the simplified version of the van Deemter equation, and recognized the possibility that the A, B and C constants might not be composed of the same terms as shown by van Deemter. For example, A was often negative, and B varied erratically with particle size.

They calculated that at 4 atm average pressure the above column would have 2000 plates per ft.

It may be that the HETP's reported above were limited by equipment factors. If the sample is charged over a long time period, the peak will be wide. The problem is to add the sample as a sharp slug and have it dissolve in the shortest possible length of column. Indeed, the advantage of small samples is they can be added instantaneously and are immediately absorbed on the first short section of column. In this view, still smaller samples ought to be still better if they could be added effectively.

Effective efficiency seems to improve if the temperature is raised continuously during the analysis. An example was given earlier for the GSC case, in which Greene and Pust worked with hydrocarbons through C_4. Dal Nogare and Bennett (624) separated the alcohols from methyl to nonyl by such a technique (Fig. 6-5). The curve shows evenly spaced, symmetrical peaks on the silicone solvent (see Chapter 7). Analytical time was greatly reduced.

The foregoing sections of this chapter have covered the effects of the key variables on column efficiency.

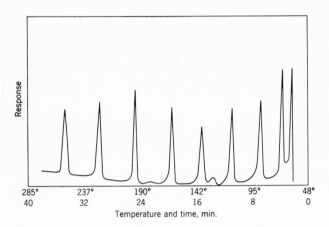

Fig. 6-5. Effect of temperature programming on peak shape.
Courtesy of Analytical Chemistry (624).

Other effects of these variables which will be discussed in
more detail later will be mentioned briefly here.

EFFECT ON PEAK SHAPE

Temperature affects peak shape by changing the
extent of solvent-solute interaction. The required operating temperature restricts the choice of solvents to those
that are not too volatile, unstable, or high melting. Temperature affects retention times, relatively and on an absolute basis. High temperature has a definite and deleterious
effect on selectivity, or the ability of the column to separate
materials according to type. Film depth affects the degree
to which solute molecules are adsorbed on the surface of the
support, which also affects peak shape.

Chapter 7

PEAK

DISTORTIONS

H. S. Knight

Shell Development Company

DISTORTED PEAKS are undesirable for several reasons.
They are broad at the base, causing overlapping of adjacent
peaks. The retention time of the peak, which is normally
measured to the peak maximum, varies with sample size.
The area is indeterminate if the curve approaches the baseline asymptotically. Finally, the area of a peak superim-
posed on the slope of another cannot be integrated automatically.

CAUSES OF DISTORTION

Distorted peaks result when $\underline{a}$ changes with solute
concentration, in other words, when the "sorption" isotherm
(including adsorption and absorption) is nonlinear. The usual GLC curve is Gaussian, with the tips of the base representing the minimum concentration of solute. If the isotherm is such that small amounts of material are dispro-
portionately held, $\underline{a}$ will be low at minimum concentration
and the tips will be retarded. The front of the peak will
merge with the bulk of the peak, causing a straight leading
edge, and the rear of the curve will be elongated, causing
tailing. If $\underline{a}$ is high at infinite dilution, the rear of the peak
will be straight, and the front elongated. This is called
leading.

In either leading or tailing, the emergence time

of the distorted peak tip depends on the $\underline{a}$ value at infinite dilution. The emergence time of the tip is therefore constant. A very small sample would emerge at that time. As larger samples are added the bulk of the peak will deviate more and more from the tip.

In GSC, adsorption is the only possible source of a nonlinear isotherm. In the great majority of adsorption studies, the isotherm is similar to the one shown in Fig. 7-1. Here small amounts of solute are very tightly held. Tailing is to be expected, and tailing is observed except with fixed gases, unless special precautions are taken. Gregg and Stock (581) were able to find GSC systems representing various types of isotherms and to show that the peak shape could be predicted from the isotherm in the way discussed here.

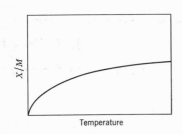

Fig. 7-1. Typical adsorption isotherm.

REDUCTION OF DISTORTION

One cure for tailing in GSC is the use of a displacement technique. For example, the carrier can be saturated with benzene, which will displace saturates and prevent them from tailing. A difficulty here is that the column is left saturated with benzene and must be regenerated prior to reuse. Another difficulty is that the displaced components emerge successively, and are not separated by carrier. Usual detection methods are not applicable unless the successive components differ in the property being detected. Markers might be found to show the zone boundaries, but this complicates the situation very seriously.

Modification of Surface. Since adsorption is a surface phenomenon it should be possible to reduce the surface or to change its nature to reduce adsorption. Minimum surface is presented by glass beads, which still cause tailing. Reacting polar surfaces with chlorosilanes failed to eliminate peak distortion (604).

White and Cowan (657) were able to make an adsorbent with a linear adsorption isotherm for certain samples by reacting the exchangeable groups in a swelling bentonite with an organic amine. They calculated the amine chain length to just cover the surface while using all the exchange capacity of the clay. A commercial product, Bentone 34 (National Lead) was found to approximate their specifications. This material gave symmetrical peaks. They obtained an HETP of 0.05 cm.

DISTORTION IN GLC

In GLC the $\underline{a}$ values could vary with concentration either because of adsorption or solution effects. As outlined above, tailing goes with a low activity at low concentration, which could occur as a result of a non-ideal solution in which γ goes down with concentration. Such low γ values result from complex formation or from differences in molecular size. Complex formation is not very common, and molecular size differences have not caused tailing in practice. For example, pentanes do not tail with squalane $(C_{30}H_{62})$ columns. Therefore, it is felt that tailing in GLC is almost always caused by adsorption.

Polar materials tail more than nonpolar ones because they are more strongly adsorbed on the common polar supports. Liquid phase data are evidence for the statement that polar materials are more strongly adsorbed in GLC. Other evidence is obtained by comparing activity coefficients from vapor-liquid equilibrium with those from GLC. Kwantes and Rijnders (606) found noticeable discrepancies unless nonpolar solutes were employed. Still further evidence is available from GLC data showing that relative retention times vary as the solvent concentration changes. This must be attributed to adsorption. Eggertsen et al. (209, 566, 567) found that not even hydrocarbons are immune to relative time shifts with solvent concentration. These data will be discussed later. Knight (604) found that even with polar solvents the new high efficiency columns are susceptible to solute adsorption. Some data for triethylene glycol solvent are given in Table 7-1, based on an assigned $\underline{a}$ value of unity for methyl alcohol.

TABLE 7-1. SOLVENT CONCENTRATION AND
RELATIVE a VALUES

Triethylene Glycol, %	MeOH	n-BuOH	Ethyl Acetate	n-Hexane
1	1.00	1.9	3.5	10
3	1.00	2.7	4.8	26
10	1.00	2.6	5.4	55

In efforts to control tailing, many of the same
techniques cited above for the GSC case have been studied.
Dal Nogare and Bennett (624) obtained symmetrical peaks
for alcohols by increasing the temperature during the analysis. The volatility of the material represented by the tail
was increased, reducing the tail. Bayer (533) converted
strongly adsorbed amino acids into more tractable materials
by esterifying the acid and converting the amine to the N-tri-
fluoroacetyl derivative.

Modification of Surface. By way of changing the
nature of the support surface, Johns (433) added small
amounts of fatty acids to the regular phthalate ester solvent
and found that the C-22 insulating brick responded favorably
to the treatment. Chromosorb (Johns-Manville) was less re-
sponsive but was inherently better than C-22, and was about
as good as the treated C-22. Knight (604) found just the reverse, that C-22 was better than Chromosorb and was less
susceptible to treatment with fatty acid. Desty (558) found
that Celite was better than C-22 from the standpoint of tailing, but was stickier and harder to pack.
Dintenfass (373) studied the effect of an adsorbed
material on the capacity of the adsorbent for another material of the same or a different type. He observed that one
acid on the surface used the capacity of the adsorbent for
acids, but not for other types of materials. In line with this
finding, it should be possible to prevent tailing of alcohols
by using a polyol solvent, but amines for example would still
tail unless an amine were also added. In practice use of any
particular solvent type is inconsistent with having available
a wide variety of solvents.

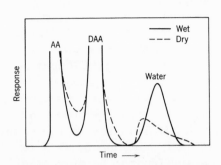

Fig. 7-2. Tailing is reduced by
satiating the surface. Courtesy
of Analytical Chemistry (604).

Modification of
Carrier. The hydrocar-
bon case is easily solved,
for any solvent seems to
prevent tailing of these
nonpolar materials. For
the more polar samples,
Knight (604) found that it
was possible to reduce
tailing by adding a volatile
material, similar in type
to the sample, continuously with the carrier. Sol-
vent selectivity was little
affected by the volatile
tailing reducer. The carrier was saturated with the added
material at room temperature, and very little of the tailing
reducer remained on the column at the common operating
temperature of 60°C. Nevertheless, the surface of the support was satiated for the particular type of material and the
curved portion of the adsorption isotherm was avoided to a
large extent. More symmetrical peaks were the result.

Fig. 7-2 shows the effect of adding water and an
amine to the carrier on the shape of water and amine peaks.
The carrier was saturated at room temperature with water
and n-hexylamine and the column (mixed solvent, see Chapter 8) was operated at 60°C. With hydroxyl-containing solvents the effect on the water peak was less marked, while
with nonpolar solvents the
effect was greater. For
example, analysis of a
blend of four alcohols,
methyl through n-butyl,
was impossible on a hy-
drocarbon solvent without
water in the carrier, at
constant column tempera-
ture. While the rising
temperature technique
solves this particular
problem it would be more
difficult to apply if the

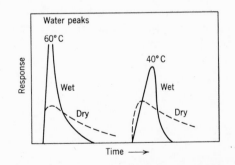

Fig. 7-3. Leading is reduced by
raising the temperature. Courtesy of Analytical Chemistry (604).

sample was not a clean homologous series, but contained close boiling isomers which might be fused into a single peak.

Fig. 7-3 illustrates the effect of temperature on peak shape. At 40°C the water peak with wet helium has a sloping forward edge, which is called leading. Elongation of the forward edge is a solution effect, which in this case results in a high   at minimum concentration. This type of non-ideality occurs when the solvent and solute differ in functional group. It is common in GLC. In severe cases the tips of the normal curve move ahead, causing the rear of the peak to be more vertical and the front to be elongated. In Fig. 7-3 leading and tailing are both apparent.

Note that leading is decreased by raising the column temperature from 40 to 60°C. Solutions tend to be more nearly ideal at higher temperatures, reducing the change in   with concentration.

Experience has shown that most common volatile polar compounds can be analyzed by GLC at 60°C with a tailing reducer to give fairly symmetrical peaks. Close control of column temperature is necessary since the amount of volatile material on the column at equilibrium will otherwise change, affecting the baseline.

The foregoing discussion of tailing has neglected the mechanical cause, the method of introducing the sample. Porter et al. (292) showed that if the sample is introduced into a chamber from which it is swept exponentially into the column tailing will result. In well-designed equipment tailing from this source is minor. However, with high efficiency columns and sensitive detectors such tailing may cause trouble. It is essential to keep dead space in the apparatus to an absolute minimum for high efficiency. (See also Chapter 10.)

Chapter 8

COLUMN

SELECTION

H. S. Knight

Shell Devolopment Company

SELECTIVITY OF SOLVENT

CONTROL OF SELECTIVITY may make it possible to place peaks for one molecular type among peaks for other types with minimum overlapping. Fredericks and Brooks (213) found that dimethylsulfolane has enough polarity to retard olefins beyond the saturates of the same carbon number, without causing them to emerge with higher boiling saturates (Fig. 8-1). Less polar materials did not retard the olefins enough.

Desty and Whyman (368) studied the separation of C_4 to C_{10} hydrocarbons on n-hexatriacontane and benzyldiphenyl. Their data for saturates are reported in terms of carbon number, which means they are not corrected for the lower boiling points of isoparaffins compared to normal paraffins of the same carbon number. They show boiling point separation of types within one carbon number, with little difference between the two solvents for alkanes. The benzyldiphenyl retarded cyclics and aromatics on a type selectivity basis. They used the information to carry out a thorough analysis of fairly pure isooctane. A few sulfur compounds were also studied.

Eggertsen, Knight and Groennings (567) studied the separation of C_5-C_7 saturates on various substrates. They used 2,2-dimethylpentane and cyclohexane as a standard pair to show selectivity of the solvents for naphthene-

69

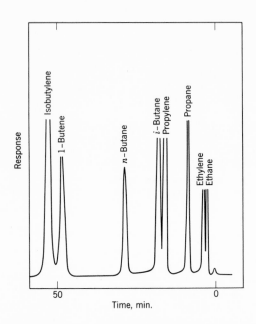

Fig. 8-1. Separation of light hydrocarbons. Courtesy of
Analytical Chemistry (213).

paraffin separation. Since these compounds have the same
vapor pressure, the retention time ratio, activity coefficient ratio, and relative volatility are all numerically the
same. Table 8-1 gives some of the data.

TABLE 8-1. NAPHTHENE-PARAFFIN SELECTIVITY
OF VARIOUS SOLVENTS

Solvent	Retention time ratio, cyclohexane to 2, 2-dimethylpentane
Silicone SF-96	1.2
Squalane	1.4
Triethylene Glycol	1.8
Dimethylsulfolane	1.9
Ethylene Glycol	2.7
β, β'-Oxydipropionitrile	2.8

On all of these liquids the naphthene was retarded. SF-96
was the most neutral of these solvents. It was shown that
the above data were typical of naphthenes and paraffins as
classes (Fig. 8-2) even though 2, 2-dimethylpentane could be
regarded as an atypical paraffin. The cluster of points below the naphthene curve near the 90 min region represents
the dimethylcyclopentanes, which are more paraffin-like as
might be expected. The branched paraffins are not more
naphthenic, in fact, Phillips (478) found that isooctane was
less strongly held on a polar solvent than on a nonpolar one,
compared to n-heptane.

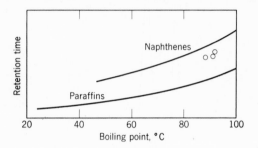

Fig. 8-2. Type separation on ethylene glycol. Courtesy of
Analytical Chemistry (566).

The practical significance of the data in Table 8-1
is as follows. The naphthenes may be completely separated
from the paraffins on the nitrile solvent if the highest vapor
pressure of any component in the mixture is less than 2. 8
times the lowest. The volatility of the highest boiling paraffin will then be greater than that of the lowest boiling naphthene.
Since practical mixtures may have greater volatility ranges than this, the above type separation by itself is
inadequate. There are not too many naphthenes in the C_5-C_7
fraction, and it might be possible to make them appear in
gaps among the paraffins. Actually the squalane solvent gave
more individual peaks than the very polar columns.

AMOUNT OF SOLVENT

Eggertsen et al. studied the effect of amount of
solvent on the support. Dry supports caused tailing, but

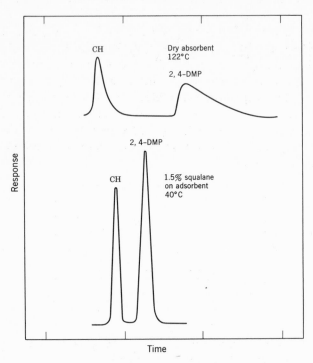

Fig. 8-3. Effect of solvent on peak shape. Courtesy of
Analytical Chemistry. (566).

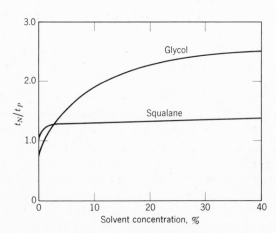

Fig. 8-4. Effect of solvent concentration on type separation.
Courtesy of Analytical Chemistry (566).

were of interest because they retarded paraffins while all the solvents retarded naphthenes (Table 8-1). It was found that small amounts of solvent eliminated tailing (Fig. 8-3) without reversing the type sequence. As more solvent was added the naphthenes were retarded more and more, until the above liquid-type columns were the result (Fig. 8-4). There was a very useful intermediate stage where no type separation occurred (boiling point separation) and another where the naphthenes, which are higher boiling than the paraffins, emerged with paraffins of the same carbon number (Fig. 8-5). The carbon number column was useful for cutting out small amounts of lower and higher carbon number impurities in the C_5-C_7 fraction, and could be used to break up this fraction as a preliminary to complete type separation.

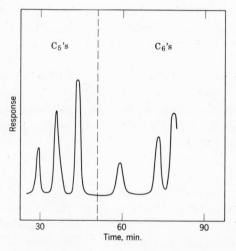

Fig. 8-5. Separation on "carbon number" column. Courtesy of Analytical Chemistry (566).

MULTIPLE COLUMNS

Another approach would be to separate a mixture on a paraffin-retarding column, trapping all of the naphthene-containing sequence. These materials could then be analyzed on a very polar column. The high boiling paraffins which would normally interfere with the type separation would be absent. Thus the volatility range for complete type separation could be increased by about a factor of two (the relative volatility of cyclohexane to 2, 2-dimethylpentane on the solid with tailing reducer is about 0. 5).

Alternatively, the combined peaks from the squalane column (which gave the most individual peaks) could be trapped and analyzed by mass spectroscopy or on another GLC column.

Eggertsen and Groennings (567) used gas chromatography on three different columns to analyze a C_5-C_7 saturates blend. By combining the data from the three columns all of the compounds were determined except for 3-ethylpentane. Separation within the naphthene and paraffin spectra varied subtly from column to column to make the overall separation possible.

Zlatkis (664) and Tenney (649) have shown that perfluorotributylamine is similar to the solid adsorbents and different from most solvents in that it retards paraffins relative to naphthenes. Mixed columns of this and other solvents could be prepared to separate the types in various ways.

The separation of C_5-C_6 olefins was studied by Knight (603). This is an interesting system because so many types are possible, including mono- and diolefins, cyclic mono- and diolefins and acetylenes, although the latter were not included in the study.

The carbon number column mentioned above was suitable for olefins, although the exceptionally low-boiling isomers were probably included with the next lower carbon number if they were present at all. The carbon number column was used to isolate the C_5 and C_6 fractions.

Adsorption could not be ruled out so a values were reported rather than solvent-solute activity coefficients. An a value of unity was assigned to 1-hexene, and with this basis only the retention times and the vapor pressures were needed to calculate a values for other materials.

On polar solvents one double bond was equivalent to closing the ring in its effect on the a value. The effect of a double bond went down as the carbon number went up, as might be expected, since polarity decreases with increasing molecular weight. Data on the polar solvent, ethylene glycol, are given in Table 8-2.

TABLE 8-2. EFFECT OF STRUCTURE ON RELATIVE
ACTIVITY COEFFICIENTS ON ETHYLENE GLYCOL

Compound	Relative $\underline{a}$ (1-hexene = 1)
n-Pentane	1.1
Cyclopentane	0.6
1-Pentene	0.5
Cyclopentene	0.25
2-Methyl-1,3-butadiene	0.2
n-Hexane	1.6
1-Hexene	1.0 (assigned)
Cyclohexene	0.5
Methylpentadienes (mixed)	0.5
Benzene	0.1

Thus the paraffins can be separated from the
monoolefins and naphthenes of the same carbon number if
the vapor pressure range covers somewhat less than a factor of two. The same is true of cycloolefins and alkenes.
Aromatics can be separated from saturates over a range of
15. Note that the solvent is very sensitive to carbon number, with about a factor of two difference between C_5 and
C_6. Cycloolefins and dienes which are together on the polar
solvent can be separated on a nonpolar solvent which retards
the cyclics.

EFFECT OF POLARITY

Illustrating the above data for the C_5's are Figs.
8-6, 7 and 8. These show the effect of increasing solvent
polarity on the type separation. For example, the low boiling hexene, 3,3-dimethyl-1-butene, moves ahead as polarity increases, until on the nitrile solvent it emerges with
1-pentene. Its higher carbon number makes it more active
on the polar solvent. Again a balance of selectivity is best,
for the dimethylsulfolane provides the most useful separation. It places cyclopentene with 3-methyl-1,2-butadiene,
which is not likely to be present.

The hexene separation was also studied, but is
not described in detail here because no new principles are
involved. It is of interest, however, that β,β'-oxydipropio-
nitrile and dimethylsulfolane happen to form different sets

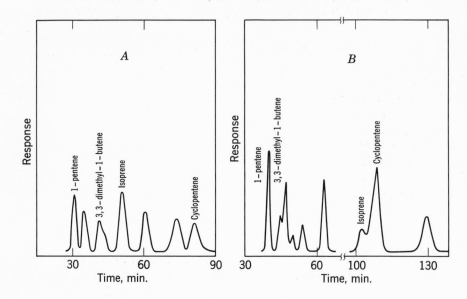

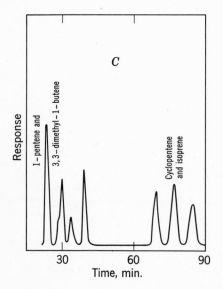

Fig. 8-6. Separation of
pentenes on columns of
increasing polarity:
A, slightly polar;
B, intermediate polarity;
C, very polar.

Courtesy of Analytical
Chemistry (603).

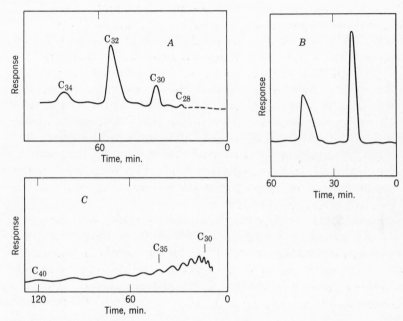

Fig. 8-7. High temperature separations: A, methyl esters at 290°C; B, benzyldiphenyl isomers at 200°C; C, crude wax at 290°C. After Adlard and Whitham (526).

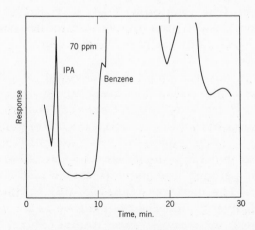

Fig. 8-8. Trace analysis with 100 microvolt full scale deflection. Courtesy of Analytical Chemistry (535).

of pairs among the monoolefins. By analyzing on both columns and combining the results, all the components are determined except for the pair, 3- and 4-methyl-1-pentene
which did not separate on any column studied. These small,
unpredictable but important shifts make it necessary to em-
phasize trial and error for selecting specific columns.

Published aromatics separations are in general
of the boiling point type. Jones (435) separated aromatics
through C_9 on Apiezon L at 297°F. It is of interest that at
the time he was able to refer to his work as high temperature GLC. Desty and Whyman (368) included aromatics
through the xylenes in their study of n-hexatriacontane and
benzyldiphenyl. The aromatics were retarded fairly strongly
on the more polar benzyldiphenyl compared to n-paraffins
of the same carbon number.

Zlatkis, O'Brien and Scholly (664) separated m-
and p-xylene on a column only five meters long. The conditions were as follows: 100°C, 60-80 mesh Chromosorb
support, 15% benzyldiphenyl solvent, 59 psi inlet pressure,
100 ml/min flow of helium, 0.005 ml of sample. The column had 9,500 plates, and the separation was 20-30% complete.

In hydrocarbon analysis little work has been done
on GLC of mixtures containing all types of hydrocarbons.
The saturates, olefins and aromatics may be separated by
liquid phase chromatography prior to the analysis, and the
sample may be fractionated by GLC or distillation. However,
the separation of saturates and aromatics by types is good
enough to suggest application of GLC directly to straight run
gasoline (649).

Much of this chapter is devoted to hydrocarbons
because most of the published literature concerns hydrocarbons. Tenney (649) studied type separations for hydrocarbon and oxygenated compound systems. His paper is outstanding as a general source of practical GLC data. He presented plots of boiling point against log relative retention
time where n-pentane was used as a standard with assigned
time of unity. His data are transferrable to other columns
of the same solvents provided n-pentane is first run on the
other column at or near the same temperature.

Tenney concludes that the dipropionitriles such
as β, β'-oxydipropionitrile are the most generally useful

solvents for type selectivity. As a neutral or boiling point column, Tenney recommended polypropylene glycol of molecular weight 2000 for oxygenates. For hydrocarbons he chose squalane. (The data of Eggertsen et al. in Table 8-1 suggest SF-96). He found that ethers were relatively easily separated from other oxygenates except acetals (80 to 90°C boiling point spread mixtures being completely separable). Alcohols could be separated from other types over a boiling point range of 15°C on a silicone column. Ketones and aldehydes could not be separated on a type basis. A technique for doing this will be presented later.

Data from other sources show that, compared to other types, alcohols are retarded on polyol solvents and emerge early on nonpolar solvents.

Compounds containing carbon, hydrogen and oxygen are the subjects of almost all the papers on GLC, with hydrocarbons claiming the lion's share. A complete bibliography would show scattered papers on sulfur compounds in petroleum, alkyl halides and so forth. Many of these are touched on elsewhere in this book. Usually these separations are by boiling point and offer no new principles.

CHEMICALLY ACTIVE COLUMNS

One paper will be mentioned here because it describes work with the very reactive boron hydrides (437). Extreme precautions had to be taken to keep oxygen and moisture away from the column during the analysis. The solvents consisted of paraffin oil, Octoil S and tricresyl phosphate, impregnated on Celite.

At the opposite pole from the above are the chemically active stationary phases for GLC. Here separation is achieved by complex formation or by chemical reaction. Silver nitrate dissolved in a polar solvent retarded Type I olefins $(CH_2{=}CHR)$ in the work of Tenney.

Kerr and Trotman-Dickinson (602) used a mull of sodium bisulfite in ethylene glycol to react with aldehydes, but not ketones. The aldehydes could then be determined by comparison with a similar separation without the bisulfite. For removing olefins, these workers used a formula of 9 parts of mercuric acetate, 3 of mercuric nitrate and 20 of ethylene glycol per 100 of support.

Phillips (478) employed low melting metal salts
as solvents to achieve some interesting separations. He reported that -picoline and 2, 6-lutidine require 250, 000
plates of silicone (1/4 mile) for separation equivalent to one
centimeter (4 plates) of zinc stearate.

MIXED SOLVENTS

Columns containing mixed solvents are often a
short-cut to finding a single solvent with the desired properties. If two solvents separate a sample in two different
ways and something in between is needed, they may be mixed. If they are unreactive they may be blended before im-
pregnation. This has the advantage that each particle of support has both solvents coated on it and any leading or tailing
reducing property of either solvent is available throughout
the column. In terms of retention times, the same effect
may be achieved by using each solvent in its own column,
and connecting the columns. This also has an advantage,
that one can be shortened if the proportions are not right.

The most complicated mixed column recalled by
the writer was used by Davis and Schreiber as the partition
column in their gas analysis work reported in Chapter 5,
and attributed by them to Block and Hochgesang. It consisted of 30 ft. of 30% solution of 23% ethyl benzoate and 77%
dimethylformamide, followed by six feet of 25% dimethylsulfolane. The first section contained the volatile solvents
which were retained by the dimethylsulfolane, so that they
did not contaminate the Molecular Sieve 5A column to be
used for the gas analysis portion of the separation. The
early section was reimpregnated in situ as needed.

Other mixed columns have included a short section of Molecular Sieves to retain normal paraffins, as described earlier. As they are adsorbents and would cause
tailing, Whitham used squalane as a tailing reducer for kerosine work. For gas oils the squalane was too volatile, but
he found that by operating the sieve portion at 320°C tailing
was greatly reduced.

Knight (604) used a blend of nonpolar diisodecyl-
phthalate and polar triethylene glycol solvents for the work
with allyl amines described in connection with tailing. The
combination produced a series of evenly spaced peaks, while

neither solvent alone was useful.

HIGH TEMPERATURE COLUMNS

In high temperature GLC the stationary phase problems that are avoidable or sufferable at low temperature are often magnified. There are more isomers to contend with, they have smaller differences in vapor pressure and in solvent-solute relationships, and the solvents available to cope with them are more restricted. Even the analysis of low boiling samples suffers if the temperature is raised. The vapor pressure ratio of ethyl alcohol to ethyl ether is 10 at $20^{\circ}C$, only 3 at $100^{\circ}C$. At the same time the activity coefficients tend to approach each other at high temperature. Thus temperature has a definite effect on selectivity. Finally, there is the problem of keeping the solute molecule itself in one piece as it passes through the apparatus.

All of these problems are alleviated by working at the lowest practicable temperature. Short columns are indicated, with fine support for maximum efficiency and low solvent concentrations. In this way a wider variety of solvents can be used. Low sample sizes are necessary, as with large samples flat-topped peaks may result. The height of the peak is limited by the vapor pressure of the material.

The effect of operating pressure has been debated in the literature. Some early workers thought that if reduced pressures were employed the temperature could also be reduced. Actually this is true only if the pressure is below the vapor pressure of the sample, and at this point there is little carrier left. The present view is that reduced pressure increases detector response by increasing the concentration of sample, but that it also increases velocity gradient, reducing efficiency. Some workers feel that the overall result is beneficial.

Felton (385) and Dal Nogare and Safranski (625) have reported successful work at temperatures up to 300-$350^{\circ}C$. They used Dow Corning high vacuum silicone grease, stabilized by pretreatment at $400^{\circ}C$.

Adlard and Whitham (526) reported a variety of high temperature separations. Their curves for methyl esters, to C_{34}, benzyldiphenyl separation into its isomers, and waxes to C_{40} are shown in Fig. 8-6.

COLUMNS FOR TRACE ANALYSIS

In trace analysis minimum columns are also help-ful, for peak width increases with retention time and low, broad peaks are less readily distinguishable from baseline noise than early, high ones. Some baseline noise is inevi-table where equipment is being pushed to its limit for trace analysis work. In the same way, it is important to select a solvent in which the trace material has a high activity coef-ficient, so that it will emerge early. Small peaks are par-ticularly difficult to measure if they are on the tail of a large preceding peak, so the activity coefficient of the major components should be low.

Where a suitable solvent is not available, it is possible to trap the impurities away from the bulk of the sample and analyze the trap contents with greatly reduced interference (368).

Bennett et al. (535) have reported a number of trace analyses. They used a DC amplifier to increase the signal from a thermistor thermal conductivity bridge. Their effective recorder sensitivity was 100 microvolts or less. Fig. 8-7 shows their analysis of benzene containing 70 ppm of isopropyl alcohol. Note that the major peaks were off scale. If insufficient attenuation is available, two runs can be made with different sample sizes and peaks common to both can be used to tie them together, or a marker can be added.

Combined high temperature and trace analysis presents a special problem in that small samples are not possible if traces are to be detected. This aggravates the high temperature problems since the temperature must be high enough to avoid flat peaks. Here might be an important use for some of the new sensitive detectors - for trace anal-ysis at lower temperatures than otherwise possible.

There is a special kind of trace analysis in which traces of relatively high boiling materials are determined in fixed gases, in particular, in air. The fixed gases sepa-rate so readily from the trace materials that no special stationary phase problems are involved.

Chapter **9**

COLUMN
CONSTRUCTION

H. S. Knight

Shell Development Company

AFTER A PACKING is available, the next problem is what
kind of material to put it in. Some common materials include copper, aluminum, stainless steel and glass. The former two have the advantage of convenience, the latter are
less reactive and possibly less catalytic. For all around
utility stainless steel is probably preferable. Most commercial equipment has stainless detector assemblies and columns. Glass is sometimes used for high temperature work,
or where U-shaped columns that can easily be repacked are
employed. Ellis and Iveson (569) used monel or nickel columns for halogens.

COLUMN GEOMETRY

The column should be as long as necessary to ac-
complish the desired separation, and no longer if time is a
factor. With modern plate efficiencies on the order of 1000
plates per ft. most problems can be solved with columns
less than 10 ft. long. For that "lone stubborn pair" consider a combined GLC-spectroscopic or two-column analysis
rather than a long column with attendant problems. However, long columns do have increased sample capacity, in
proportion to the square root of the length (439) and larger
cuts can be taken. For gas analysis long columns will continue to be desirable.

83

There is no comprehensive study of column diameter that takes high efficiency columns into consideration.
Probably 3/8 in. standard tubing is little worse than 1/4 in.
with larger sizes falling off in efficiency. However, Evans
et al. (570) report that columns up to 75 mm in diameter
show no loss in efficiency under their conditions. They packed their 16 ft. columns with Celite impregnated with the solvent, and employed special vaporization chambers and detectors designed for high gas flow for the larger sizes. With
mass spectroscopy and micro-infrared techniques, large
columns are seldom needed for purely analytical purposes.

Straight and U-shaped columns are less likely
than coils to permit channeling as the packing settles, and
can be easily repacked if desired. However the writer is
unaware of any evidence that coiled columns are less efficient, and coils will continue to be used for convenience and
compactness.

PACKING THE COLUMN

The following technique for preparing columns is
probably used by the great majority of gas chromatographers
with but minor variations.

The support is weighed into an evaporating dish.
The nonvolatile solvent is weighed in a suitable vessel and
dissolved in enough volatile solvent to wet the support. If
two nonvolatile solvents are to be used it is often preferable
to blend them at this point. The solution is added to the support and the mixture stirred on a steam bath (a hot plate is
slower) until the packing looks dry. Fine packings particularly tend to spatter during this operation. Continue the drying with occasional stirring until the odor of the volatile solvent is gone. Do not use a vacuum oven unless the high boiling solvent is certain to be nonvolatile under the oven conditions.

Place a plug of glass wool in one end of the tubing
and pour the packing in the other end through a funnel, vi-
brating the column with a massage vibrator, or eccentric,
or tapping it vigorously on the floor the while. If the column
is long it may be bent into a U and packed from each end.
When it is full to within one cm from the top, pack the re-

maining space about half full of glass wool.

During these operations record the weights of the materials used, so that the data may be reported in a suitable manner.

N. B. Do not pack the column with dry support and impregnate it in situ unless experience has shown that an efficient column will result. One 20 ft. column so impregnated had only 1000 plates.

Chapter 10

SAMPLE INTRODUCTION

S. A. Greene and E. F. C. Cain

Rocketdyne Research

IN GAS CHROMATOGRAPHY, sample introduction and sample size are extremely important because of their influence upon the apparent retention volume, the shape of the peaks obtained, and subsequently upon the ability of a given column to separate the components of the sample. Several authors (5, 117, 316) have discussed the theory of gas chromatography and utilizing the plate theory of Martin and Synge (5), and Porter, Deal and Stross (292) have studied the problem of sample introduction and sample size in gas liquid partition chromatography. The plate theory of Martin and Synge involves several simplifying assumptions which are as follows:

1. Samples are charged to the head of the column so that the initial charge is instantaneously contained within the first theoretical plate.
2. The partition coefficient for the distributing material is constant throughout the column.
3. No change in the volume of a volume element of mobile phase occurs as it passes through the columns.
4. All rate effects can be taken into account by the concept of theoretical plates.

The first two assumptions are important when considering sample introduction. By utilizing equations which describe the concentration of the solute as a function of the volume of the eluting gas, two extreme cases were considered. The first case has been designated "plug" flow and corresponds to a plug of solute gas mixture of constant composition being charged to the head of the column. The other case corresponds to mixing of the mobile phase in a vaporizer in such a manner as to introduce the vapor without dilution to the head of the column initially, but the sample concentration falls off exponentially with time to zero. Mathematically, plug flow gives rise to symmetrical peaks while exponential flow gives rise to peaks having a definite tail. In practice, the normal method of sample introduction will be somewhere between the two cases which have been considered.

Porter et al. (292) compared elution curves, which were calculated on the basis of "plug" flow and exponential flow, with an elution curve obtained by means of their instrument which had a sample introduction system

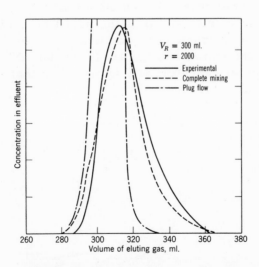

V_R = 300 ml.
r = 2000
———— Experimental
— — — Complete mixing
—·—·— Plug flow

Concentration in effluent

260   280   300   320   340   360   380
Volume of eluting gas, ml.

Fig. 10-1. Comparison of experimental and theoretical elution curves, assuming a retention volume of 300 ml and 2000 theoretical plates. Courtesy of Journal of the American Chemical Society (292).

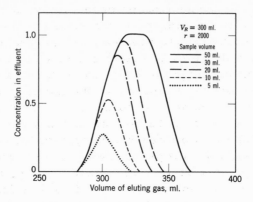

Fig. 10-2. Elution curves for variable sample of constant concentration. Courtesy of Journal of the American Chemical Society (292).

containing a heated vaporizer block at a distance from the column head. The sample was introduced into the heated vaporizer block, vaporized at some indeterminate rate and carried to the column head by the mobile phase. The experimental conditions were chosen such that the activity coefficient was nearly unity and thus the partition coefficient was nearly constant throughout the column. The results of this comparison are shown in Fig. 10-1. It should be noted that the experimental curve closely approaches that calculated for exponential flow.

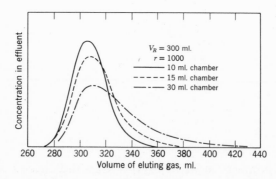

Fig. 10-3. Elution curves for constant sample size with variable charging time. Courtesy of Journal of the American Chemical Society (292).

Porter et al. calculated the effect of varying the sample size while holding the concentration of the sample in the mobile phase constant. This corresponds to varying the sample size under "plug" flow conditions and the results of this calculation are shown in Fig. 10-2. These authors have also considered the variation of charging time at constant sample size for exponential flow. The results of this calculation are shown in Fig. 10-3.

It is obvious from the above discussion that to obtain maximum column efficiency and accordingly narrow sharp peaks, the sample should be as small as possible and introduced in a high concentration as a "plug" flow.

The use of a small sample size should also be considered on the basis of the activity coefficient of the sample in the stationary phase. If a perfect solution is formed between the sample and the stationary phase, the resultant chromatographic peak is symmetrical if the other assumptions which have been stated previously are valid. However, as is often the case, the sample does not form a perfect solution with the stationary phase and tailing or leading can

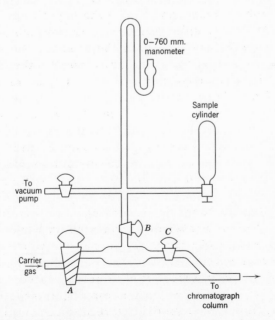

Fig. 10-4. By-pass system. Courtesy of Analytical Chemistry (475).

result, but if the sample is small, the resultant concentration of the sample in the stationary phase approaches extremely low concentrations and ideality. That is to say, if under a given set of chromatographic parameters, an unsymmetrical peak is obtained, the resultant peak can be made more symmetrical by reducing the sample size.

BY-PASS AND VALVE SYSTEMS

The introduction of gaseous samples into a gas chromatograph has generally been accomplished by means of either a "by-pass" system or a six port gas sample valve. Both of these systems are designed to introduce a known volume of gas sample into the mobile phase. The simple "by-pass" system used by Percival (475) is shown in Fig. 10-4. By calibrating the sample volume between stopcocks A, B, and C an accurately known quantity of sample can be introduced into the instrument in the following manner:

1. Place stopcock A in the reverse position to that shown in Fig. 10-4, and close stopcock C. The mobile phase now flows through the pass line.
2. Attach sample cylinder to the system, open stopcock B, and evacuate the system.
3. Disconnect vacuum and introduce the sample into the system to the desired pressure as read from the manometer.
4. Isolate the calibrated sample volume by closing stopcock B.
5. Introduce the sample into the column by simultaneously reversing the position of stopcock A to that shown in Fig. 10-4, and opening stopcock C.

Other authors (189, 575) have used similar systems which allow for interchangeable sample volumes and make the operation of only a single stopcock necessary to introduce the sample.

Most commerical instruments have employed a modification of the six port gas sampling valve. Fig. 10-5 shows a diagram of one modification of this type of valve which is available commercially. The gas sampling valve is generally connected to some type of gas handling system which allows the sample to be introduced into the valve with-

out contamination. The sample size is determined by the
volume, the presure and the temperature. Referring to the
diagram, the sample is introduced into the sample valve,
when the valve is in position 1. When the desired sample is
contained within the sample volume tubing, the valve is
moved into position 2. At this point the mobile phase sweeps
through the sample volume introducing the sample into the
chromatograph in a condition which approaches "plug flow".
The major advantage of this system over the by-pass system
is that while it can be connected to a gas handling system
and used in the same manner as the by-pass system, it can
also be used in a gas stream, where repetitive sampling is
desired.

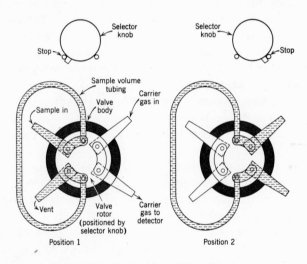

Fig. 10-5. Precision gas sampling system. Courtesy of
    Perkin-Elmer Corporation.

        Tenney and Harris (507) have developed a gas
pipet method of sample introduction. However, since this
method has been used more commonly in liquid sample introduction, it will be discussed in detail later. Smith,
Swinehart, and Lesnini (642) have described a system in
which standard vacuum stopcocks, (hollow, precision-
ground, 2 mm, oblique bore) have been used as a gas sample introduction system. Lubricated syringes have also

been used to inject a gaseous sample into a chromatograph, but this method is relatively crude and is recommended only for qualitative analysis.

LIQUID SAMPLES

The satisfactory introduction of liquid samples has in general been more difficult because of the limitation upon sample size. The most common way of introducing a liquid sample has been by means of a syringe and hypodermic needle. The sample is injected through a self sealing serum cap into the head of the column or into a vaporization chamber from which the sample is rapidly vaporized and carried by the mobile phase to the head of the column. The major problem encountered with this method of sample introduction is the difficulty of the mechanical introduction of an extremely small liquid sample into a relatively high pressure gas stream. The use of 1/4 ml syringes has been common but not very satisfactory since the generally desired liquid sample size is approximately 10 microliters. Recently, micro syringes having 10 microliters capacity, as well as smaller sizes, have become commercially available, and have proven to be very satisfactory in most cases. (See Appendix I B).

As mentioned previously, the liquid sample is generally introduced through a serum cap to the head of the column or into a flash vaporizer. If a small liquid sample is injected into the head of the column in such a manner that the tip of the hypodermic needle is level with the top of the column packing and the sample is injected very rapidly, ideal and desired conditions are approached very closely. However, if the sample is introduced into the space above the column packing, the sample introduction conditions will be somewhat less ideal and the separation will tend to be impaired. A simple diagram of this type of sample introduction system is shown in Fig. 10-6.

If, however, a flash vaporizer system is used, the sample is introduced by means of the syringe through a serum cap into a heated vaporizer block through which the mobile phase is flowing. The vaporizer is maintained at a temperature sufficient to insure rapid vaporization of the sample. During this period, the mobile phase is trans-

porting the vaporized sample to the column head. The result of this system is that the sample is introduced to the
column at some indeterminate rate. However, since the
sample size is generally very small, the influence of rate
is minimized and the system is satisfactory.

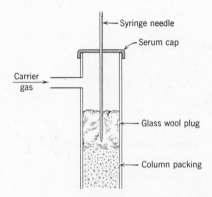

Fig. 10-6. Sample introduction to column head.

The main difficulties which have been encountered
with syringe sample introduction are the small sample size,
reproducibility, and problems associated with time lags
which change retention times. The advent of commercially
available micro syringes has allowed a much closer control
of sample size than was possible with the standard 0. 25 ml

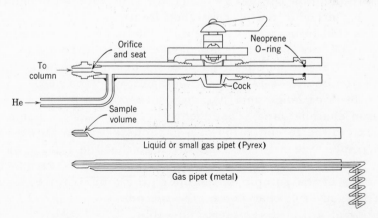

Fig. 10-7. Micro-dipper system. Courtesy of Analytical
Chemistry (507).

syringe. The problem of introducing a reproducible sample
volume has not been completely solved with the micro syringes, but a precision syringe, which has a reported accuracy of 0.1% and interchangeable capacities of 0.005, 0.01,
0.02, 0.03, 0.04, and 0.05 ml is also available commercially.

    Tenney and Harris (507) have developed a preci-
sion liquid sample introduction system which is shown in
Fig. 10-7. The sample introduction system is attached to a
heated vaporizer block and operates as follows: The large
cock is cracked slightly allowing the mobile phase to flush
air from the system to the outside past the "O" ring. After
the special pipet is filled by means of capillary action, it is
slowly inserted into the tube until the pipet handle forms a
seal with the "O" ring. The large cock is completely opened
and the sample in the pipet is now under the pressure of the
mobile phase in the chromatographic system. The pipet is
now inserted through the large cock until the tip is in con-
tact with the orifice and seat, at which point a differential
pressure across the pipet is developed and the sample is
swept into the heated vaporizer block and subsequently to
the column. The authors report a precision at the 95% con-
fidence level of $\pm$ 0.89% using a pipet of 0.00159 ml capacity. In the same manner, gas samples can be introduced by
means of a gas pipet which is also shown in Fig. 10-7.

    A third method of precision sample introduction
was reported by Dimbat et al. (198). The method depends
upon the introduction of a weighed liquid sample which has
been sealed into a glass ampoule. The prepared ampoule is
introduced into a special "by-pass" sample introduction system which is equipped with a bellows crusher. The sample
expansion chamber is isolated and can be evacuated. The
ampoule is crushed and the sample vaporized into the expansion chamber and subsequently introduced in a manner
similar to the introduction of a gaseous sample. However,
the sample size must be controlled so that the final pressure in the sample volume does not exceed the saturation
pressure of the sample at the operating temperature. While
this method is cumbersome, the introduction of a weighed
quantity of a liquid sample is possible.

    The sample introduction systems, which have
been discussed, have proved satisfactory for many applica-

tions. However, as the use of the gas chromatograph has increased, special sampling and sample introduction techniques have been reported. It is impossible to review all of them in this short discussion, but a survey of several new techniques will serve as a guide to possible variations on standard methods or to the development of new techniques.

SPECIAL TECHNIQUES

In the field of organic chemistry, gas chromatography has been used to separate materials of high molecular weight and to determine the n-paraffin distribution in waxes. Ogilvie et al. (629) introduced the sample by injection from a hypodermic syringe through a rubber serum cap. The samples for which high temperature gas liquid chromatography is used are usually either solids or viscous liquids. To introduce this type of sample, the sample and the syringe were heated by an infrared lamp until the sample was fluid enough to be drawn through the needle. The sample introduction was made immediately while the sample was still liquid. An alternate procedure was to dissolve the sample in a lower molecular weight solvent which would have a relatively short retention time and would not interfere with the desired analysis. Care must be taken to use a hypodermic needle long enough to introduce the sample onto the hot portion of the column. Dal Nogare and Safranski (625) used similar methods of sample introduction in their work with high temperature gas liquid chromatography. Quin and Hobbs (635) also employed the solution technique of sample introduction by introducing a methanol solution containing a few milligrams per milliliter of the esters of nonvolatile acids directly into the chromatograph.

Because of sensitivity of the gas chromatographic technique, it has been applied to the field of trace analysis. Eggertsen and Nelson (568) determined the C_2 to C_5 hydrocarbons from engine exhausts and the atmosphere. The sample sizes used ranged from a few hundred milliliters of exhaust gas to 5 to 10 liters of air. The samples were passed through a trapping column at liquid oxygen temperatures to concentrate the samples. After the sample was collected in the trapping column, it was connected to the separating column while still cold and purged with helium for 20 to 30 min. This removed most of the material boiling below the C_2 fraction. After flushing, the trapping column was quickly warmed and the sample was eluted through an Ascarite column to remove water and carbon dioxide from the sample and then through the separating column. This system emphasizes two techniques which have been employed in gas chromatography sampling. The first is the use of a trapping column to concentrate the sample and the second is the use of an auxiliary precolumn to remove interfering substances.

West et al. (656) have proposed the use of cold activated charcoal columns to collect trace quantities of organic air pollutants. The cold collecting columns are transferred to the chromatograph and the sample introduced directly from the collecting column to the analyzing column. The method was applied satisfactorily in the range of 1 to 50 ppm of organic air pollutants with an efficiency of approximately 80%.

Boggus and Adams (539) employed a gas liquid chromatograph as the concentrating system in the analysis of chloroethane. A 1 ml liquid sample was introduced into the concentration chromatograph by means of a gas sampling valve. The separation was carried out and the trace contaminants collected in a U-tube which was immersed in liquid nitrogen. The U-tube was then fitted onto the second chromatograph, warmed, and the contaminants were analyzed directly. It was reported that materials in concentrations as low as 1 ppm could be determined.

Simmons and Snyder (641), however, employed two or more gas chromatographic columns in series such that the preliminary cuts obtained from the first chromatograph could be charged directly into another chromatograph. This arrangement of instrumentation allows the detailed analysis of a complex mixture without having to prepare separate samples.

From the above discussion, it is apparent that sample introduction and sample size are parameters of gas chromatography which can be varied to meet the desired conditions of the analysis and that judicious choice of the techniques which are employed can have a large effect upon the results of the analysis or separation which is being carried out.

TEMPERATURE
CONTROL

C. M. Drew

U.S. Naval Ordnance Test Station

THE TRANSPORT VELOCITY of a sample component through a column is directly dependent upon the distribution of the component between the stationary and moving phases. Separations are only possible where there is a different distribution between the compounds under consideration. The distribution is also a strong function of temperature and the column must be operated somewhere between the two limits of distribution, i.e., where the compounds are completely adsorbed in the stationary phase or completely desorbed. Obviously no separations could be achieved under conditions of either of these extremes. Increasing column temperature will shift the distribution more in favor of the moving phase and thereby increase the transport velocity of all the sample components. In order to utilize the maximum effectiveness of the stationary phase it is necessary to choose a temperature low enough that the sample constituents are mostly distributed in favor of the substrate. Under these conditions the transport velocities will be small and the analysis will take a long time. Also, the peaks will be broad with resultant losses in sensitivity (peak height). In practice a compromise in temperature is selected to give reasonable analysis times without undue sacrifice in column resolution.

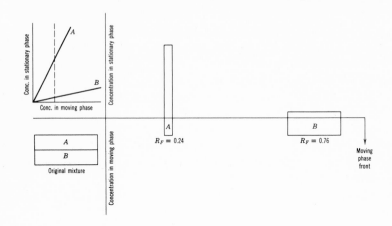

Fig. 11-1.   Ideal linear chromatography.   Courtesy of
Reinhold Publishing Corporation (439).

GENERAL CONSIDERATIONS

Fig. 11-1 is a graphical representation of the
separation of two compounds assuming ideal linear chromatography (439).   This model involves only the essential features of chromatography.   The band shape during its passage
through the column does not change.   Compounds A and B
introduced originally at the head of the column as a mixture
behave independently of each other and are separated only
on the basis of their different partition coefficients.   For a
more thorough treatment of this subject, the reader is re-
ferred to Keulemans (439) and Wilson (4).

Effect of Temperature on Resolution.   The effect
of three different column temperatures upon a group of sev-
en hypothetical compounds chosen for a wide boiling point
range is depicted in Fig. 11-2.   The resultant chromatograms
so obtained are given for each example, but non-ideal chromatography was assumed in the latter instance so that the
chromatograms would appear in their more conventional
form.   This model demonstrates the effect of column temperature where a wide range of boiling points are encountered, and further shows that no one temperature can be chosen
to give a complete analysis.   This is a typical problem en-

countered with many sample mixtures. In many cases it is not necessary or even desirable to analyze all the constituents so a temperature is chosen that will achieve the separations desired within a reasonable time.

Where it is necessary to have a complete analysis with an excessively large boiling range it is necessary to analyze duplicate or multiple samples at different temperatures or use tandem columns selected to complement each other. For example, the Perkin-Elmer Vapor Fractometer, Model 188, utilizes as many as three columns simultaneously. Another technique described later is continuous heating of the column during the analysis, a feature which is available on the Burrell Corporation Kromotog models.

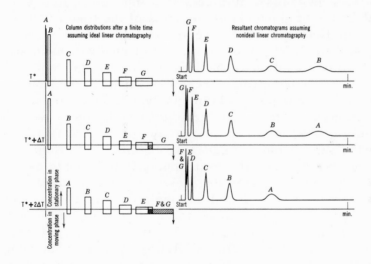

Fig. 11-2. Effect of column temperature on the resolution of a wide range sample.

Martin (271) recognized the potential of gas chromatography as a tool for the measurement of solution parameters such as partition coefficients, activity coefficients, effective vapor pressures, or Henry coefficients and heats of solution or vaporization. This is a different application for gas chromatography but it does provide basic information which is valuable for extending the analytical application of the method. Porter et al. (292) point out that the

heat of vaporization of the solute predominates in determining the change in partition coefficient with temperature, and
that reasonable estimates of partition coefficients as functions of temperature can be based upon a single-temperature
point. This would, in principle, allow the worker to predict
an optimum column temperature or to determine, in the case
of continuous heating, the temperature range over which the
column should be operated.

COLUMN STABILITY AT HIGH TEMPERATURE

Relatively brief attention has been given to the
longevity of column packings in the literature. It is quite apparent that the vapor pressure of the liquid substrate must
be low enough at maximum column temperature to prevent
volatilization of appreciable amounts of the liquid. Furthermore, the liquid should be thermally stable for reasonable
periods of time, since any chemical change will have serious
effects on its resolving behavior. Another important consideration is the possibility of reactions between the liquid substrate and the compounds being analyzed. Occasionally such
interactions are utilized to facilitate resolution or detection
but general practices rely primarily on physical factors to
effect the separation. In general, chemical reactions which
alter the character of the partitioning liquid should be avoided. Weak complex formation (solvation effects) on the contrary, are often very useful and their chemical reversibility
insures no permanent damage to the stationary phase will
result. Such an effect was used by Bradford et al. (110)
specifically to retard terminal olefins by weak adduct formation with silver nitrate. In this case an upper temperature
limit of about $40^{\circ}C$ was imposed by the effect of temperature on the stability of the complex.

Migration of Substrate. One of the most serious
problems encountered in high temperature chromatography
is loss of stationary phase by migration of the liquid
through the column packing (weeping). The problem is particularly pronounced with large diameter columns used in
preparation work. The best solution is reduction in the
amount of stationary phase. Simple calculations will show
that adequate coverage of the surface area of the support

can be realized with only a few percent of liquid by weight.
This does introduce some loss in column capacity since the
volume of liquid substrate must be considered as well as
surface area, but it must be remembered that under operating conditions the surface molecules of the liquid are those
mostly involved in the process. These effects are treated
in Chapters 4 and 5. The only other purpose for adding larger amounts would be to supply a reservoir from which losses
could be tolerated for some time before depletion of the liquid from available surface. Actually, this only aggravates
the weeping problem, and the residual film after the bulk of
the liquid has evaporated or migrated away is undoubtedly
held with more tenacity. One suggestion made to the author
(683) is to place a short section of dry support material at
the column exit. This provides for a time extension on the
column life since any liquid migration will first have to saturate the uncoated surfaces before reaching the column exit.

  This approach was criticized by Van der Craats
(365). He feels that the loss of stationary phase is by evaporation and that there is no reason for condensation again.
This view is correct insofar as it applies to evaporation
losses at the exit end of the column. However, the phenom-
ena of liquid exuding from the exit bears testimony to actual
migration of liquid. Obviously a dry section will delay such
a liquid front for a time. Furthermore, the mechanism for
migration of the liquid substrate undoubtedly involves an
evaporation condensation cycle - exactly the same process
accounting for transport of the sample constituents along the
column packing. Any appreciable vapor pressure of the liquid substrate would subject it to transport by the moving
phase just as any other material in the column.

  Another plausible explanation for the transport of
the stationary phase is the solution effect of the sample constituents at high concentrations such as encountered in preparative columns. The condensation or solution of large
amounts of sample components produces bands in the column of increased wetness on the packing with resultant decreases in the viscosity of the stationary phase, hence an
increase in its mobility. Friction between the more mobile
liquid film and the moving gas phase is more effective in
driving the fluid along the packing. Other properties related
to mobility such as capillary attraction, liquid diffusion

effects, and gravity are also more effective.

In some of the earlier publications workers reported stationary phase concentrations as high as 40% of the liquid by weight of inert support. The average value at the present time is probably around 20%. For high column temperatures the amount of liquid is frequently lowered to 10% or less.

For conventional detectors the column temperature is limited to a value just below that which produces excessive base line shift due to the presence of stationary phase in the carrier stream. This limit is quite arbitrary depending upon the choice of operators, but usually a rate of carry over not exceeding 1 mg per min is typical. For more sensitive detectors the limit is held to around 1 mg per hour. These limits would be considered quite excessive by many workers.

When the column temperature is programmed steadily upward during analysis the upper limit is reached when the base line takes a definite upward swing. At this point heating is stopped.

COLUMN CONDITIONING

Techniques for preparing columns require a high temperature conditioning treatment as part of the procedure. This serves to drive off residual solvents and other volatile contaminants. It also helps distribute the stationary phase over the inert support, and in some instances drive some chemical changes to completion that would ordinarily effect column behavior at lower temperatures. The author's experience shows that a bake should be done at maximum temperature with the exit of the column open (not connected to the detector or exit line) for about one hour with a normal or moderately higher than usual carrier flow rate. After noticeable vapors have been driven off, the exit line is then connected to the detector and the adequacy of bake out is judged by the detector output, i.e., the output observed when pure carrier is in both arms of the detector. Some workers recommend conditioning up to 24 hours in order to obtain reproducible column behavior. The time required is, of course, a function of the nature of the stationary phase, and it might be safe to state that any column showing change after 24 hours is probably unsuitable for use and would never settle down satisfactorily.

APPARATUS REQUIREMENTS

Since numerous methods have been employed for controlling column and detector temperature, only brief mention will be made here of some of the methods in common usage. The physical apparatus employed for this purpose is relatively unimportant so long as it provides for adequate control, convenient change of columns, and rapid change of operating temperature. In general, the temperature of a column should be controlled throughout its entire length to within $0.1^{\circ}C$. If peak height measurements are used for quantitative estimations the temperature control is highly critical. Retention volumes are similarly quite temperature dependent, and where these are used to measure solution parameters or to calibrate columns, very careful attention must be given to the quality of temperature control.

Long Columns. Glass columns were first employed in the earlier developments of the method, and since it is not feasible to bend glass tubing after packing, it was necessary to use reasonably long straight sections. Two or more of these sections were then joined after packing with suitable connections to afford longer column lengths. Since glass tubing is commercially available in about four ft. lengths, it was common to use them as received for chromatography columns. In order to provide temperature control the thermostated region was necessarily a long narrow enclosure. This geometry does not lend itself readily to critical temperature control because of difficulties in uniform heat input and temperature distribution over such large areas. Curiously enough, there still is some tendency among manufacturers of commercial equipment and designers of self-made equipment to use long narrow enclosures. This is partially justified by the convenience offered in the storage of large numbers of straight four ft. long columns, and the quick change feature offered by such instruments as the recently introduced Pye Chromatograph.

Temperature regulation of long thermostats has been achieved nicely, however, by more than one method. The first arrangement employed was to surround the column in a jacket fed with vapor from a constant boiling liquid (61, 89, 128, 137). The apparatus operates under total reflux with provision to return the condensate directly to the boiler. With suitable lagging it offers a very precise means of providing uniform temperature. Disadvantages in this method lie in the excessive warmup times, inconvenience of changing temperature, restriction of operating temperatures to the availability of liquids having the desired boiling points, and the difficulty of finding liquids stable enough or with high enough boiling points to operate at the higher column temperatures. Also, large amounts of hot boiling liquids are hazardous.

Another method frequently used even in modern equipment is an air bath provided with rapid circulation (321, 334). This method is also used by the author with a coiled column and will be described later.

Coiled Columns. Another common arrangement is the use of block heaters with the column in close enough proximity to the block (a suitably shaped mass of high heat conducting metal) to assure adequate temperature distribution. This method has many variations. Two examples of commercial equipment using modifications of this scheme are the Consolidated Chromatograph, and the Pye Argon chromatograph.

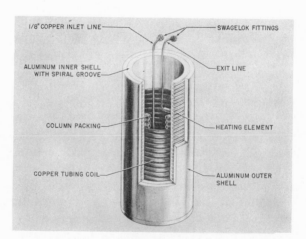

Fig. 11-3. Arrangement for programming column temperature. Courtesy of Butterworths Publications (203).

Fig. 11-3 is an example of an earlier model used by the author for continuous heating of the column. This apparatus is still in use by our laboratory; however, the circulated air bath arrangement mentioned above is a better method because the large mass of metal has been eliminated and this permits more rapid cooling or heating of the system and gives better temperature distribution. Columns have been thermostated by direct immerson in bath fluids or in refrigerants having suitable boiling or melting points. This method is entirely suitable but not in general usage.

One of the more direct approaches to the problem is the adaptation of a standard laboratory drying oven for the column and detector enclosure as in the Cenco Vapor Phase Analyzer.

A very compact and efficient unit specifically designed for high temperature work was devised by Felton (385). He made ingenious use of glow plugs as detector sensing elements incorporated within the same heating block used to control column temperature. Felton states, "In use the unit is wrapped with electrical heating tape or placed directly in a suitable oven. "

TEMPERATURE CONTROL OF DETECTORS

Combined Control. The majority of analyses done by gas chromatography are at a fixed column temperature. For many detectors it is necessary to maintain them at a carefully controlled constant temperature. This is most conveniently done by including the detector assembly in the column thermostat. This has a further advantage of permitting very close coupling of the column exit line to the inlet arm of the detector. This arrangement can on occasion lead to objectionable condensation of high boiling fractions or liquid substrates within the detector cell block. A common practice is to supply a small additional heat input to the detector so that it will control at a few degrees higher than the column itself. This minimizes the condensation problem to a large extent.

Separate Control. An alternative scheme is separate thermostating of the detector from the column assembly. This method is highly recommended by the author since it allows changing column temperatures without involving the temperature dependence of the detector. With this practice the detector is maintained at a higher temperature than the column.

There are some detectors whose output is not seriously affected by temperature changes. These include all the various ionization and hydrogen flame detectors discussed later. The main temperature requirement in this case is that of preventing condensation within the detector and adjacent lines between the column exit and detector inlet. A secondary requirement such as with rare gas (Argon) ionization system is the choice of a temperature compatible with optimum detector sensitivity to the sample constituents. It is interesting to note that with this detector improved sensitivity is observed at moderately high operating temperature, whereas with the more conventional thermal conductivity cells elevated temperatures generally produce losses in sensitivity. This is particularly true with thermistor type units. The seriousness of the effect can be judged from a recent Gow-Mac brochure accompanying their various detectors. Typical response curves are given in Fig. 11-4.

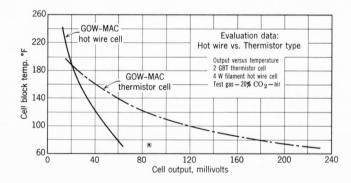

Fig. 11-4. Comparison of temperature on the output of
thermistor vs. filament type detector.
Courtesy of Gow-Mac Instrument Company.

VARIABLE COLUMN TEMPERATURE

Numerous articles have appeared in which continuous heating of the column is employed in order to obtain useful analysis over a wide span of boiling points (42, 203,

225, 491, 550, 587).

The author has employed this technique exclusively for a number of years in its application to the kinetic
study of gas phase reactions (203). The convenient spread
of elution peaks so obtained and the increased over-all resolution have been much superior for this type of sample mixture than results obtained with the constant temperature techniques. Continuous heating of the column can be more time
consuming per sample than constant temperature chromatography because of the slow heating rate required in order to
utilize effectively a reasonable column length and the necessity of returning the system to its original starting temperature for each analysis. The method has also proven generally unpopular because of several difficulties in maintaining
zero base line drift. Most detectors employed in the United
States measure thermal conductivity of the column effluent
and they are quite temperature sensitive. Therefore, as
mentioned earlier, they must be thermostated separately
from the column. They are also somewhat flow sensitive
but more important, if the pressure in the reference and
measuring sides change relative to each other, the detector
output changes. If the column temperature changes the viscosity of the carrier gas changes as an inverse function of
column temperature, thus changing the pressure drop
through the column. This effect is discussed by Clough (550).
The resultant change in column flow is reflected as changes
in back pressure in the measuring chamber of the detector,
thus producing drift. Clough solved the problem by using a
flow control device instead of a pressure regulator.

Although flow regulation ahead of the column is an
effective means of overcoming these difficulties, the author
uses a method which is equally effective and much simpler,
and at the same time affords better column efficiency.

The problem of flow control is caused by dependence on the pressure drop through the column packing for
establishing the flow rate. In practice an inlet pressure is
chosen that will give the desired rate with the exit stream
near or about atmospheric pressure. The variable flow
problem has been solved by virtually eliminating the pressure drop through the column. An orifice is placed in the
exit line and thermostated with the detector at constant temperature (Fig. 11-5). An inlet pressure considerably in

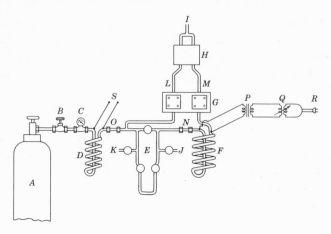

Fig. 11-5. Schematic arrangement for an apparatus permitting programmed heating of the column.

A.   Helium Supply
B.   Pressure Regulator
C.   Pressure Gauge
D.   Purifying Trap
E.   Introduction System
        Valve Assembly
F.   Column
G.   Flow Control Blocks
H.   Detector
I.   Exit Line to Flow
        Meter and Traps

J., K.   Vacuum Connections
L.   Reference Stream
M.   Column Effluent
N., O. Glass Inserts between
            Swagelok Fittings
P.   6-Volt 5-Amp Filament
            Transformer
Q.   5-10 Amp Variac
R.   110-V AC Power Supply
S.   Switch to Provide Cur-
            rent to Bake out Puri-
            fying Trap

excess of that required to give adequate flow through the column is used. The orifice is restricted until the desired flow is obtained, hence the column is pressurized throughout its entire length and up to the orifice at essentially the inlet pressure. Actually, there is still some pressure drop through the column, but with a suitably high inlet pressure this is reduced to some negligible value. The exit line of the column is 1/8 in. thin wall stainless steel. The orifice is made by compressing this line between two metal blocks with tightening screws until the desired flow is achieved. There is enough resiliency in the metal tubing to allow for

some plus or minus variation; however, it is advantageous
to leave the orifice at a fixed setting, thus assuring reproducible flows over extended periods of time. Measurements
with a soap film flow meter have verified constancy of flow
for well over a period of one year at a given inlet pressure.
If another flow rate is desired, it is most easily achieved
by changing the inlet pressure rather than adjusting the orifice. Wide variations require adjusting both or even install-
ing a new line between the blocks and readjusting for the desired rate. The use of valves is not permissible because
enlargements in the exit line produce sample dilution with
carrier gas. This affects both resolution and sensitivity.

In addition to achieving base line control over extended temperature changes, column operation is improved
due to the increased pressure of the carrier gas and the low
pressure drop through the column. These effects have been
treated in Chapter 4.

In Fig. 11-5 it will be noted that the exit lines from
the measuring and reference arms of the detector block are
connected to a common exit line after leaving the detector.
A very slight restriction to flow is placed in this line to assure that both arms of the detector are at the same pressure,
thus utilizing the fact that both arms of the thermal conductivity cell have nearly identical sensitivity coefficients of
pressure. In the author's apparatus no appreciable base line
drift is encountered over a column temperature range from
-196° to $100^{\circ}C$, using a flow rate of 50 ml/min with 50 psi
inlet pressure on a 14 ft. column packed with a 30-40 mesh
particle size column material.

Since the importance of close column temperature
control has been stressed in order to achieve maximum efficiency, it might appear that a closely controlled temperature program would be required for this technique. The difficulty of achieving this has no doubt discouraged many workers from using the method. It has been shown that the ratio
of peak height to peak width is a strong function of column
temperature. It is well known that peak areas, on the other
hand, change very little with column temperature. Area
measurements have proven to be more reliable for quantitative accuracy, hence close column temperature control is
necessary only where utmost column efficiency is required.

OPTIMUM OPERATING CONDITIONS

With programmed heating, consideration must be
given to optimum carrier flow rate and length of column as
a function of heating rate. Ideally, at the start of an analysis all of the constituents of the sample mixture are con-
densed at the front end of the column. Incidentally, this insures a perfect start condition and eliminates the problems
of band broadening brought about by failure to inject the sample properly. As the column warms, the most volatile material reaches a vapor pressure great enough to begin incipient
migration through the column and it moves out ahead of the
lesser volatile materials which presumably are still stationary. This is a thermal separation not realized to such a
large extent at constant temperatures. Materials of nearly
identical boiling point must depend upon the more recognized
parameters affecting separations by gas chromatography.
It is readily seen that as the temperature increases the transport velocity of any given material increases accordingly
since the distribution of the solute is shifted into the moving
phase and correspondingly less in the stationary phase. The
upper limiting transport velocity is reached when all of the
solute is in the moving phase. At this point the velocity of
the solute is equal to the velocity of the carrier gas. If this
happens before the solute reaches the end of the column the
remaining length of column is not effective and only serves
to broaden the band. Each successive fraction will experience about the same acceleration and reach its limiting velocity at about the same point in the column. The column
should be just short enough to prevent this state being reached prior to emergence from the exit end. It is obvious,
therefore, that there is a relation between optimum column
length and heating rate, and that both these parameters are
also dependent upon the flow rate of the carrier gas. These
variables could conceivably be expressed mathematically in
such a way as to allow the worker to predict his best operating conditions. At best this would be difficult even if the
present status of chromatographic theory would permit such
treatment. An empirical approach is relatively easy. Table
11-1 shows a set of operating conditions which are typical.

TABLE 11-1.   OPTIMUM PARAMETERS FOR A
1/4 IN. x 14 FT. COLUMN

Column packing: 30-40 mesh, 1.5% Squalane or Pelletex
Column dimensions: 1/4 in. OD by approx. 3/16 in. ID by
                                    12 ft. long
Column material: Stainless steel tubing
Carrier gas: Helium
Inlet pressure: 50 psi
Flow rate adjusted
 by exit restriction: 50 ml/min
Heating rate: -196°C to 100°C/90 min (nonlinear)

With these conditions it was found that an 8 ft. column was
less effective than a 12 ft. column, and no harmful effects
could be observed with column lengths up to 15 ft.; however,
this seemed to be the longest length that could be tolerated
without noticeable loss in resolution due to excessive band
broadening. The broadening effect was most serious with
olefins which exhibit some tailing on this packing. A 30 ft.
column operated under these conditions gave poor results
with obvious spreading occurring in the unusable additional
15 ft.

COLUMN HEATING APPARATUS

The physical arrangement for cooling and heating
the column can be achieved in a number of ways. One method mentioned previously in the text (Fig. 11-3), consists of
an aluminum block provided with an embedded nichrome
heater. The entire assembly is contained in a Dewar flask.
Liquid nitrogen or other refrigerant is poured into the central opening until a suitably low temperature is achieved,
after which it is removed and immediately the heater is
turned on, controlled by a variable transformer set to give
the desired heating rate. Since heat losses to the surround-
ings are minimized by the surrounding Dewar, the heat capacity of the system is the determining factor on the rate of
heating versus voltage applied. Over reasonable ranges of
temperature the rate of rise is reasonably linear. This system has worked satisfactorily for a number of years, but it
is unduly time consuming since the large heat capacity of the

block requires a long time for cooling, and it also wastes considerable refrigerant in the cooling process. The purpose of the block is merely to provide a means of heating the column and distributing a uniform termperature along the column by means of the high heat conductivity of the aluminum metal. The latter was not achieved very satisfactorily because the lower end of the block was slow to heat, and temperature gradients of several degrees were obtained along the column, depending on its location within the block.

A different arrangement for this technique is shown in Fig. 11-5 and in the photograph, Fig. 11-6. The column is a 14 ft. length of coiled stainless steel pipe 304 1/4 in. OD by 3/16 in. ID. It is suspended in an air bath

Fig. 11-6. Self heating column arrangement used for programming temperature during analysis.

consisting of a stainless steel Dewar which surrounds the assembly. A circulating fan is provided which is held on a shaft made from stainless steel tubing. The shaft is supported by two bearings located above the bath and driven by a pulley arrangement. Stainless steel construction was chosen because of its low heat conductivity. No bearing assemblies are located within the bath, thus eliminating possible troubles with bearing lubricants which have to withstand wide temperature limits. The hollow shaft permits removal of excess refrigerants by suction. The column itself is the heater. It has an electrical resistance of approximately 2.4 ohms at 25°C, hence an applied 6 volts will furnish 2.5 amperes heating current, which is sufficient to heat the column and bath through a temperature rise of 100°C within a few minutes. One end of the column must be electrically insulated. The other end is a common ground. The insulation was achieved by inserting a length of 1/4 in. OD by 2 mm ID capillary glass tubing in the inlet line between two Swagelok fittings, using nylon or Teflon ferrules. This is shown in the photograph, Fig. 11-6. The column heating current is supplied by a filament transformer which delivers 6 volts output with an input of 115 volts AC and rated for 5 amperes capacity. A Variac transformer is used to supply the input to the filament transformer, thus providing for control of the column heating rate.

A similar coil arrangement packed with highly activated charcoal is used to purify the helium carrier gas. It can be heated in the same manner with an electrical switching circuit to apply full current to the coils. This provides for a convenient bake out. During use the coil is immersed in liquid nitrogen and effectively traps impurities in the helium. With Grade AA helium it will remain effective for several days' usage between bake out. This purification is necessary when columns are started at -196°C because impurities in the carrier gas, such as air, collect on the column while it is sufficiently cool.

Although several difficulties are encountered with programming temperature, the foregoing text has shown that most of them are easily solved. There are outstanding advantages to be realized using the technique which easily outweigh any of the other difficulties that are encountered. The ability to analyze mixtures having a wide range in boiling point is its chief asset. Fig. 11-7 is a typical example of a chromatogram obtained with the method (564). It can be seen that there is good retention for each compound with an acceptable ratio of peak height to width - in other words, there is no crowding and lack of column efficiency for low boiling fractions and no objectionable broadening and loss

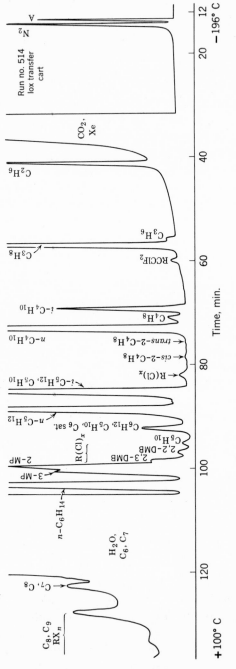

Fig. 11-7. Analysis of impurities in Aviators' Breathing Oxygen using continuous column heating.

Column: 1/4 in. x 14 ft.   Carrier gas: Helium (50 ml/min)

Packing: 1.5% Squalane on 30-40 mesh Pelletex

of sensitivity for high boilers. The convenient time displacement between fractions permits easier trapping where recov-
ery of the fractions is needed. For example, if the low boilers emerge as a series of rapid sharp spikes in a few sec-
onds' time, it is virtually impossible to change traps quickly
enough or to anticipate the location of an emerging fraction
in relation to the trap and detector. Also, all fractions utilize the available number of theoretical plates with equal efficiency, regardless of their boiling point, since they undergo roughly the same history of distribution between the moving and stationary phases during their journey through the
column packing.

      With this technique the stationary phase is not
subject to maximum temperature for extended periods of
time. In practice the temperature is elevated until all sample components are driven off or until the vapor pressure
of the stationary phase rises to a high enough value to cause
base line drift; thus the column is automatically baked out
between runs.

      The use of low column temperatures permits se-
lection of adsorbants which normally have low retention for
the sample fractions. Separation at these lower temperatures avoids undesirable reactions on the column, such as
deuterium-hydrogen exchange reactions, degradations, or
polymerizations. If partition columns are used with this
technique their lower limit of operation is just above or
nearly equal to the freezing point of the stationary phase.
Usually freezing of the liquid film has very harmful effects
on the column efficiency, and for this reason most very low
temperature work is restricted to gas solid chromatography
or packings of the liquid modified solid adsorbant type.

Chapter 12

DETECTORS

C. M. Drew

U.S. Naval Ordnance Test Station

IT MAY BE SAFE to assume that as much emphasis has
been placed on the development of detectors for gas chromatography as the total time spent on all other aspects of the
method. The development of reliable high sensitivity detectors has no doubt been largely responsible for the phenomenal growth of gas chromatography. Methods of detection
are quite numerous, and they vary in complexity from a
simple gas burette to a time of flight mass spectrometer.
The sole purpose of the detector is, as the name implies,
that of detection of sample constituents. It should respond
continuously in a reproducible manner to changes in the
composition of the eluent gas from the column without hys-
teresis. It should be quite sensitive to these changes and
linear in response.

There are two basic types of detectors; those that
respond to changes in concentration as the first derivative,
i.e., differential detectors, and those that respond to the
accumulative change, i.e., integral detectors. The first
detectors employed were of the integral type; however,
modern methods use differential detectors because of their
greater sensitivity and the easier interpretation of the chromatograms obtained. For quantitative results the integral
of the change in column effluent is necessary; consequently
various methods have been devised to integrate the output of
the differential detector. This will be dealt with later as a
special problem related to detection.

James and Martin have been accused of publishing their first practical papers in obscure journals from the standpoint of general interest; however, it should be recognized that most tools of the researcher arise from acute need, and no other field is faced with such formidable analytical problems as biochemistry. Many significant advances in chromatography, even the latest super-sensitive detectors, have arisen from the efforts of biochemists, hence it is this author's feeling that the results were quite properly published in the Biochemical Journal, and the fault, if any, lies in the failure of others to notice these earlier developments in the specialized field and attach proper significance to the results. James and Martin first separated a series of fatty acids and devised a method to continuously titrate and record the appearance of the acids in the carrier stream with time. The result was an integrated record of the change in column effluent. This detector is now regarded as primitive and suitable only for materials which will ionize in solution, but it established the prime requisite for sensitive detection, i.e., that of ignoring the carrier gas completely and sensing only sample constituents. All methods of detection rely on some manner of eliminating carrier gas signal. The ultimate sensitivity is limited in part to the degree with which this is established.

The most straightforward solution to nullifying the carrier gas signal was employed by Janak (68) and Van der Craats (189). They used carbon dioxide for the carrier gas and passed the column effluent into a burette or a pressure responding device after passage through a dilute aqueous solution of potassium or sodium hydroxide, thus physically removing the carrier gas. Sample constituents were not absorbed by the caustic solution, hence they could be measured as they accumulated. A plot of volume accumulated versus time gives the typical integral form chromatogram. The method is perhaps the ultimate in simplicity and the easiest and least expensive to acquire. It is restricted to comparatively large sample sizes and materials that will not dissolve in or react with the caustic solution. Also, in its present form it requires manually recording the results. The problem of automatic recording by this method was solved by Janak (251) using a pressure responding servomechanism to collect and record the fractions. In view of

the relatively low sensitivity and the amount of effort involved to duplicate this system, such an approach is no longer
justified.

DIFFERENTIAL DETECTORS

Gas Density Balance. Martin and James also re-
ceive credit for the first high sensitivity differential detector. The detector is an ingenious network of channels in a
copper block (Fig. 12-1) which compares the relative densi-
ties of the measuring and reference gas using a differential
thermocouple anemometer sensing device. The network of
channels is mechanically equivalent to a Wheatstone bridge
circuit, and has been described in terms of this analogy by
Munday and Primavesi (278). At balance there is no flow
through the anemometer. The device is adjusted to balance
when both arms of the bridge contain only pure carrier gas.

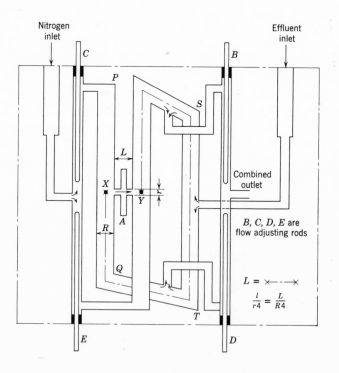

Fig. 12-1.   Diagram of Martin's gas density balance.
           Courtesy of Reinhold Publishing Corporation (439).

When the gas in the measuring side changes in density due
to a sample constituent entering the measuring side, a
slight flow is set up in the anemometer which shifts heat toward one of the thermocouples at the expense of the other.
A significant feature is that only pure carrier gas flows
through the anemometer, thus the detector responds with
very linear behavior, and its calibration (peak area) is directly proportional to the density of the sample constituent.
The high price of this detector has discouraged its general
usage. It is doubtful if the price will ever be significantly
lowered due to the extreme difficulty in manufacturing it.

Thermal Conductivity. The method of detection
most commonly used at the present time depends upon thermal conductivity changes in the effluent. Most commercial
instruments use this type of detection. These detectors are
easy to build and give sensitive response without the necessity of using amplifiers. Some employ hot wire filaments
for sensing elements and others use more sensitive thermistors. They have a further advantage of not requiring
complicated electronic circuitry unless extreme efforts are
made to improve signal to noise level. In operation they are
much like a Pirani gauge, but used to measure concentration
changes in the surrounding gas while held at constant pressure rather than the usual application of the Pirani for measuring pressure changes. The detector in its simplest form
consists of two heated sources arranged in a bridge circuit
with two reference resistors and trim resistors provided
for final balancing of the bridge. One source is kept in pure
carrier gas and the other is placed in the column effluent
stream. Thus again the principle of nullifying the effects
due to carrier gas have been utilized by a cancellation arrangement. The widespread use of this detector coupled
with the fact that it is the least expensive and most readily
available form on the market today justifies considerable
attention in the text to this method of detection.

PRINCIPLES OF DETECTION
BY THERMAL CONDUCTIVITY

The sensing elements of a katharometer are heated sources which change temperature as a function of the

thermal conductivity of the environmental gas. The electrical resistance of the source is in turn a strong function of
its temperature. These sources can be wire filaments such
as platinum, tungsten or any wire material having a suitably
high temperature coefficient of resistivity. Or they can be
semi-conductors which have much higher temperature coefficients under some conditions but of opposite sign.

   In order to realize optimum response characteristics, the effects due to detector geometry, block and filament temperatures, bridge linearity, current input, and the
thermal properties of the environmental gas must be viewed
over the wide range of operating parameters likely to be encountered. In most instances these parameters fortunately
combine to give surprisingly good response; however, a
critical examination reveals that the system is quite complex, and that it has very definite limitations. Some appreciation for these shortcomings will enable the worker to
cope with possible difficulties he is likely to encounter, and
also point out the futility of certain attractive practices that
would at first appear to be fruitful.

   Carrier Gas. First we will consider the environmental gas. Detection by this method depends upon thermal
conductivity variations in the gas as a function of composition. Let us assume that the column is operating ideally and
each sample constituent is completely separated and emerges
from the column mixed only with the carrier gas. This then
involves changes in the thermal conductivity of the resultant
binary mixture (carrier plus pure component) as a function
of composition. The subject of additivity of thermal conductivities of binary gas mixtures has been of considerable interest over a number of years, and it is well known that the
additivity is not a linear function with composition. Also,
the thermal conductivity of a binary mixture can change in a
surprising way with temperature and with carrier gases
which have conductivities not too different from the sample
constituents. Peak inversions can occur due to a change in
sign between the relative conductivities of the carrier gas
and of the mixture under measurement. The effect was discussed by Bohemen and Purnell (541) in the special case of
nitrogen carrier gas with various light hydrocarbons. In
general, this trouble can be avoided by choosing a carrier

gas of much higher conductivity than the sample constituents. This not only eliminates peak reversal problems, but provides some gain in sensitivity as well. In the United States helium is a popular choice since it has a very high conductivity, it is non-reactive, and does not interfere with subsequent analysis of recovered gas chromatography fractions.

Some countries cannot readily obtain helium; therefore they must choose some other carrier gas. Hydrogen compares favorably with helium in having a very high conductivity, but there seems to be some reluctance to use it with katharometer detection because it is potentially reactive with the materials in the column. Furthermore, it offers some explosion hazard. Nitrogen has been commonly employed as a carrier gas in the United Kingdom countries. Its thermal conductivity is much closer to most compounds of interest, hence there is a sacrifice in detector sensitivity with its use. The sensitivity change, however, is not directly proportional to the ratio of thermal conductivities of the carrier gases as might be supposed. For example, the ratio of conductivities of helium over nitrogen is about 6 at $0^{\circ}C$, which would predict a gain in sensitivity of this magnitude when using helium in place of nitrogen. In actual practice gain factors of about 2 or 3 can be realized. The explanation for this is due partly to the effect of the higher thermal conductivity upon the lowering of temperature difference between the source and the detector wall.

Detector Noise. Noise sources commonly encountered with katharometer detection are thermal convections around the filament, improper flow control around the filaments (turbulence), vibrations, stray electric signals or improper shielding and grounding, electronic noise from power supplies, and temperature variations in either the detector block or components of the associated electric circuitry. In the latter case it is important to design the circuit around the components having very low temperature dependence. Many detectors employ external reference resistors and trim resistors in portions of the Wheatstone bridge circuit exposed to ambient temperature. Special care must be exercised in the choice of these components, not only from the standpoint of materials and construction, but in their physical arrangement. Reference resistors should be made of the best quality low temperature response resistance wire annealed after winding, and placed in close proximity to each other on a massive metal core having a high thermal conductivity. Another satisfactory arrangement utilizes four sensing elements which make up all four arms of the bridge circuit. These are arranged in push-pull with the measuring arm resistors and reference resistors on diagonally opposite legs of the bridge. Since no external resistors are needed the external circuit design is simplified. This is a feature of many commercial detectors. Thermistor detectors usually employ reference resistors but are wired within the detector block so that they are thermostated with the measuring elements. Any of these methods are suitable from the standpoint of noise suppression.

The mechanical noise encountered in detectors arises from vibration of heated elements. With long straight wire filaments this is particularly troublesome. Earlier models used weight loading or spring tensions to keep the wires taut. Modern filament detectors use wire such as kovar or tungsten wound into compact coils. This improves rigidity and at the same time reduces internal dead space. It also permits easy replacement since they can be mounted on insulated threaded inserts. Thermistors are small beads of semiconductor material and they are mounted in a similar fashion.

Thermal noise is eliminated by carefully thermostating the detector assembly. This can be done in the same thermostat used for the column or in a separate one. The use of metal blocks for the detector body serves to distribute heat uniformly throughout the detector system and prevents momentary gradients around the filaments. The use of low heat conductivity materials around the filaments such as glass has proven very unsatisfactory.

Electrical noise is perhaps the most troublesome to overcome. The power supply used must be selected with great caution and batteries, if used, must be kept in a good charge condition. For critical suppression of noise careful attention must be given to shielding and grounding of the components.

Circuit Design. There are several bridge arrangements that can be employed with thermal conductivity detectors. Four examples are given in Fig. 12-2 by Dimbat et al. (198). These authors recommend arrangements B and D using relatively high external reference resistors in order to minimize current changes in measuring elements. A typical circuit diagram is given in Fig. 12-3.

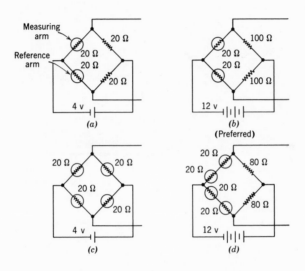

(a)

(b)
(Preferred)

(c)

(d)

Fig. 12-2 Wheatstone bridges for two and four cell thermal conductivity detectors. Courtesy of Analytical Chemistry (198).

Considerable attention has been given to proper circuit design by the various manufacturers of detector systems and optimum circuit requirements are dependent upon many factors such as cell geometry, resistance values of the elements, operating temperatures and current requirements, column performance characteristics, recorder impedence, recorder span and recorder speed. Most of these involve electronic theory which is beyond the scope of this text; however, in general these properties must be chosen to allow as nearly as possible a detector response that instantaneously and reproducibly follows changes in the composition of the column effluent as a direct linear function of composition. This requires that the thermal conductivity is also a linear function of composition which in the case of dilute concentrations of, for example, hydrocarbons in

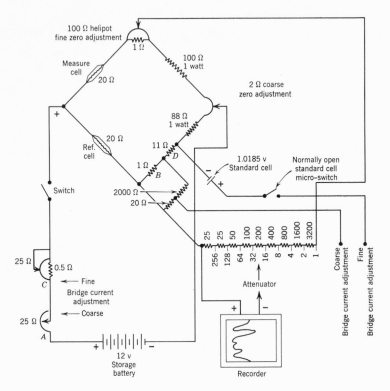

Fig. 12-3. Schematic wiring diagram for 12 volt 200 ma.
bridge for thermal conductivity detector.
Courtesy of Analytical Chemistry (198).

helium, is a resonably valid assumption.

DETECTOR SENSITIVITY

Most workers feel a need for adequate comparison between the various models and types of detectors available today. There have been some attempts made to provide
for a common basis for comparison, perhaps the most not-
able being the sensitivity parameter proposed by Dimbat et
al. (198).

$$S \text{ (ml x mv per mg)} = \frac{A \times C_1 \times C_2 \times C_3}{W}$$

where S = sensitivity parameter

A = peak area, sq. cm

C_1 = recorder sensitivity, mv per cm of chart

C_2 = chart speed, min per cm

C_3 = flow rate at exit of column, ml per min, corrected to column temperature at atmospheric pressure.

W = weight of component, mg

Recently the author conducted a survey of the leading suppliers of gas chromatography equipment known to him, and requested performance data and other related characteristics of their various detectors in the above units. It soon became apparent that such a comparison was relatively crude because the value S as determined by this means depends upon several other factors not taken into consideration. The most important of these are: the effect of the nature of the compound under detection (i. e. , molecular weight or structural effects), the choice of carrier gas, and the associated circuitry. As a result this parameter was ignored by most companies or answered with reservations. The response characteristics for several different compounds are given in terms of this parameter in Fig. 12-4 for a sensitive thermistor detector (639).

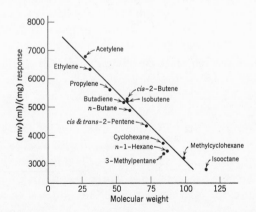

Fig. 12-4. Response characteristics of a thermistor type thermal conductivity detector. Thermistors 8-10,000 ohms at 25°C. Temperature, 22°C. Courtesy of Loe Engineering Company.

For filament detectors values up to 1500 are reported for compounds of this class where bridge voltages of the order of 12-13 volts DC are employed and helium is employed as the carrier gas. Although rough comparisons between thermal conductivity detectors and others such as the Martin density balance can be made by use of this parameter, it is pointless to use it for evaluating the more recent super-sensitive detectors. With these detectors the above criticisms apply even more strongly since their output can change exponentially with some of the factors not taken into consideration. There are indications that under specific conditions these detectors will provide S parameters of the order of 10,000 or higher.

Detection Limits. The least discernable signal from a sample trace above the inherent background noise is the sensitivity limit. This term is usually expressed in parts of component (taken at unity) per parts of carrier gas, and it is useful in that it places the lower limit on the amount of material needed for a significant measurement. For accurate work it is obvious that one should work with sample sizes sufficient to give response considerably above this limit.

Molar Response Characteristics. The relative response of both filament and thermistor detectors using helium gas has been measured for a variety of compounds against a standard measured response from benzene (486, 686):

It was shown that there exists a linear molar response within a homologous series, and that the relative response is the same for both thermistor and filament conductivity detectors.

For quantitative work these linear relations can be used instead of direct calibration. In practice the response for any compound of known molecular weight and structure can be predicted from the measured response to benzene provided the slope of the molar curve is known and at least any one compound in the particular homologous series is known relative to benzene.

In principle this property could also be used to assist in structure or molecular weight determinations. (See

Chapter 13).

TIME CONSTANT

One of the most important parameters of detector performance is its time constant. Ideally the detector should respond at an infinite rate to changes in the composition of the effluent gas. Although this cannot be achieved it is possible to build detectors with rapid enough response to introduce no significant errors in the display of the elution peak. This is done by keeping internal passages small, using low heat capacity sensing elements, and providing for rapid exchange of the effluent gas entering and leaving the region surrounding the sensing elements. In designing detectors for low time constants the sensitivity of the elements to changes in carrier gas flow must be minimized in order to reduce noise or base line drift due to flow variations. This requires some compromise in design between an arrangement where the gas stream passed directly over the elements or enters the chamber containing the elements by diffusion. Fig. 12-5 is a schematic representation of these detector designs (198). Detector A is a direct pass type with a low time constant but with objectional flow sensitivity. Detector B is a diffusion type having low flow sensitivity but too long a time constant. Detector C is a compromise arrangement which satisfactorily approaches the time-sensitivity requirements. One of the best solutions to this problem is the Gow-Mac Pretzel design, Model 9285, which divides the gas stream equally between parallel passages and places the sensing elements in connecting tubes between these passages. The carrier gas flow rate largely determines the time constant and flow sensitivity; however, this rate is determined by column performance requirements, rather than detector requirements. For this reason detectors must be designed for specific flow rates. For large column work requiring excessively large flow rates a bypass arrangement can be provided to shunt only a small portion of the measuring gas through the detector. Perkin-Elmer Vapor Fractometer models employ this technique with their preparative scale columns, thus utilizing one detector for widely varying flow conditions.

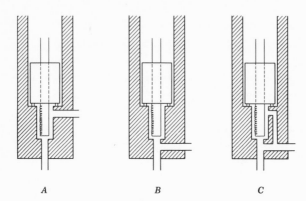

Fig. 12-5. Thermal conductivity cell designs. Courtesy
of Analytical Chemistry (198).

A. Flow through
    cell
    Time constant.
    1 second
    Flow sensitivity.
    1 μv. per ml.
    per minute
    change in one
    cell

B. Convection-
    diffusion cell
    Time constant.
    20 seconds
    Insensitive to
    flow changes

C. Self-purging
    cell
    Time constant
    10 seconds
    Insensitive to
    flow changes

Schmauch (692) has recently studied the effect of
detector response time and flow sensitivity upon the adequacy of representation of column resolution in a chromatogram. He used a mathematical model of a chromatogram
band in addition to experimental approaches to show a quantitative relation between band shape and the ratio of response
time to band width. He has shown that for adequate representation of a band the ratio of response time to band width
must have a value of 0.2 or less. In this work he expresses
response time in the conventional manner; the time in sec-
onds required for the detector to respond to 63.2% of the
ultimate output caused by a sudden transition to a differential but fixed concentration of a binary mixture entering the
inlet of the detector. He uses a measure for band width
which is somewhat unconventional in chromatography work,

but nonetheless valid for the purposes of his mathematical model. It is one-half the band width at 60.7% of maximum and is, in fact, the standard deviation term, σ, of the equation for a normal distribution curve.

DETECTOR SENSITIVITY AND COLUMN PERFORMANCE

It has been clearly demonstrated that column performance is enhanced by using smaller sample sizes. Also, column efficiency is improved by reducing column diameter as well as increasing column length, but diameter reduction also requires sample size reduction because of the resultant decrease in plate capacity per unit length of column. The limiting sample size is dictated by the sensitivity limit of the detection system, and as a result a large amount of effort has been devoted to increasing detector sensitivity. There are some commercial detectors on the market using thermal conductivity which have very sophisticated engineering to suppress background noise, thus permitting a higher signal to noise level. Most modern instruments possess these features to some extent. The highest sensitivity claimed at this time for thermal conductivity detection is one part component in 10^7 parts carrier gas. This detector is marketed by Barnes Engineering Company, and uses flake thermistor sensing elements in conjunction with careful thermostating of cell temperature.

SUPER SENSITIVE DETECTORS

The difficulties encountered in pushing thermal conductivity detectors to greater limits has reached a point where further development is not practical. Recently new detection principles have been discovered which have completely revolutionized the analytical capabilities of the method. Almost concurrently with the development of such detectors came the introduction of capillary columns by Golay (395, 577). With such columns efficiencies of 200, 000 theoretical plates have been obtained and the necessity of using microgram quantities of sample mixtures also requires detection in the super sensitive range.

The forerunner of these detectors was a simple glow discharge ionization device described by Harley and

Pretorius (229). In general, these detectors all employ
changes in the electrical conductance of the effluent gas
brought about by various methods of ionization. The Harley-
Pretorius model produces the ionization by applied DC potential between two electrodes. The sample constituents entering the detector admixed with carrier gas produce very large
changes in ion concentrations, hence very large changes in
electrical conductance can be realized. High signal to noise
ratios can be readily achieved. These detectors give varying amounts of success depending upon conditions of cleanli-
ness, current and voltage applied, and the nature of the carrier gas used, and the type compounds being measured. In
general, their characteristics seem to vary rapidly with use,
obviating their application to quantitative work. Pitkethly
(632) described a rather successful version, using a pair of
neon glow bulbs arranged in a bridge circuit. He outlined
conditions required for reproducible results, and although
his model met with some success, it proved troublesome
compared to the more recent types.

Ryce and Bryce (490) adapted the ionization pressure gauge in an ingenious manner. They chose helium for
the carrier gas because of its high ionization potential, i.e.,
24 volts DC. They operated the tube at an applied potential
of 18 volts which was ample to ionize any materials commonly encountered, but low enough to prevent ionization of the
carrier gas. In this way the current output of the tube was
due almost entirely to the ionization of the sample molecules.
Since this device relies upon thermionic emission it is sensitive to changes in the emission characteristics of the filament. Also, the tube was necessarily operated in a region
where the output efficiency was quite sensitive to changes
in the filament current, thus requiring a self-regulating current supply. Quantitative accuracy is not easy to obtain under these conditions. It is doubtful if this method was ever
developed to give performance which was as reliable or as
sensitive in response as the two more recent Lovelock (613)
or McWilliam and Dewar (619) ionization detectors. Lovelock developed an ionization detector using a different method of ionization. This detector uses a radioactive source
with argon carrier gas. The argon is excited to its meta-
stable state by beta radiation from the source which has a

strength of about 80 millicuries. The source can be either
radium or strontiom-90, the latter being more desirable.
The excited argon does not ionize, hence, with an applied
potential between an anode and cathode up to 2-3000 volts
there is essentially no current produced by the carrier gas.
When an ionizable substance enters the detector there is an
energy transfer from collision with metastably excited argon
atoms to produce ions which are in turn accelerated to the
cathode by the applied potential. The amount of current so
obtained is dependent upon the applied DC potential, thus
the sensitivity of the detector can be changed over very wide
limits. With high molecular weight compounds sensitivities
of over 100,000 times that of conventional thermal conductivity detectors have been realized. This highly successful
system is rapidly appearing on the market by numerous instrument companies. The sensitivity of the Lovelock detector is quite high for large molecules, but for hydrocarbons
under molecular weight 100 and many inert or permanent
gases the sensitivity falls off very rapidly. It is almost completely insensitive to air, for example.

Recently Lovelock (612) published some details of
his detector designed specifically for use with Golay columns.
He considerably reduced the internal dead space, thus achieving an acceptable time constant for column flow rates of the
order of 1 ml per min. This detector permits usage of capillary columns with 1-3 microgram size samples and column
efficiencies of 200,000 theoretical plates have been achieved
(699).

FLAME DETECTORS

A very simple detection method is based on the
temperature changes of a hydrogen flame measured with a
thermocouple located in the flame tip (301,324). The hydrogen feeding the flame is combined with effluent gas from the
column. An instrument using this principle is now commercially available with a claimed sensitivity of about ten times
greater than conventional thermistor type thermal conductivity cells.

This method has been used quite successfully for
a number of years by Desty and co-workers at the British
Petroleum Institute, but the method seems to have enjoyed

little appreciation in the United States because of the reluctance to use hydrogen, and perhaps a general distaste for
burning the separated fractions in a flame.

FLAME IONIZATION DETECTOR

Probably the most sensitive detector yet devised
was introduced in its infant form by Pretorius. He used a
hydrogen flame detector, but measured instead the electrical conductivity of the flame by inserting two electrodes in
the flame with an applied voltage of around 150.

McWilliams and Dewar later described a much
improved model using two flames, one in reference gas and
the other in the column effluent in which the respective electrodes were incorporated into an electrometer tube bridge
circuit operating at 500 volts DC. Further gain in signal to
noise was achieved by diluting the flame gas (hydrogen) with
large amounts of nitrogen. Several instrument companies
are currently developing this promising method. The first
one appearing on the market was recently announced by Perkin-Elmer Corporation. This detector offers higher sensitivity in the lower molecular weight range than the Lovelock
detector, and is particularly suitable for capillary columns
because it has essentially no dead space. The column effluent is fed directly into the hydrogen-nitrogen blend feeding
the flame.

The excellent merits of this system can be appre-
ciated from Fig. 12-6 which shows the separation of the nine
isomers of heptane from a 2 microgram sample.

This chapter does not pretend to cover all methods
of detection that have been used, but rather covers most of
the forms which have enjoyed widespread recognition and
those leading to the development of the more recent types.
There are many ways of looking at a mixture of gases appearing at the exit end of a column, and certainly any property of this mixture which changes as a function of composition could be adopted for measurement purposes. The passage of the gas stream into such instruments as infrared
and ultra violet absorption spectrometers, mass spectrometers, nuclear magnetic resonance spectrometers, emission spectrographs, etc., are finding important use for specialized work in gas chromatography. In general, these

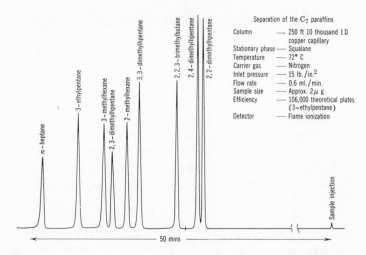

Fig. 12-6. Separation of the C$_7$ paraffins. Courtesy of Desty, British Petroleum Institute.

instruments lack sufficient sensitivity to allow their direct application in the sense that a detector is used. Most laboratories recover the separated fractions by condensation from the exit carrier gas and submit the recovered fraction to such instruments for additional study. For work with material involving isotopic tagging the combined use of gas chromatography with mass spectrometry offers an extremely useful combination (206).

INTEGRATION

Differential detectors display each fraction as a peak which represents the change in composition in the binary mixture, carrier plus sample component, with time. The area under this peak (above base line) is directly proportional to the amount of component producing the signal. Methods for integrating chromatography peaks are quite numerous and an extensive treatment of this subject is beyond the scope of this book. Since detector output is involved, integrations can be considered as part of a detection system designed to display the chromatogram on a numerical basis.

Since strip chart recorders are commonly employed to display detector output they can be adapted to furnish the peak integral. A variable drive output can be attached

to the slide wire capstan so that at base line an output shaft
has zero rotation, but the shaft rotation increases in a direct linear relation to the amount of deflection above base
line. This shaft then drives a counter or pipping pen arranged to record along the edge of the chart. The counter reading or the number of pips observed during the passage of a
peak is the integrated value. Ball and disc integrators have
been used for this application.

Other methods use electronic instruments which
couple directly to the detector output or derive their emf
signal from an extra slide wire in the recorder. A suitably
designed Watt-hour meter can be used in this manner.

The author uses an electronic integrator which
amplifies the detector output with a chopper stabilized DC
linear amplifier and feeds the signal to a condenser whose
charge build-up can continue until it reaches a potential
sufficient to fire a tube. When the tube becomes conducting
it discharges the condenser. The rate of tube firing depends
upon the detector output emf and each tube pulse trips an
electronic counter circuit. Provision is made to zero the
count rate for base line and clear the counters between peaks.
Such a system is not dependent upon the recorder span, and
thus eliminates the necessity for keeping large peaks within
the recorder scale. Most suppliers of gas chromatographs
can supply either their own integrating system or one modified for use with their instruments.

Chapter **13**

ANALYTICAL
METHODS

R. L. Pecsok
University of California, Los Angeles

APPLICATIONS OF GAS CHROMATOGRAPHIC METHODS now run into the hundreds and a critical review is no longer within the scope of a single author. A literature search is already time consuming even for a specific application. The bibliography in Appendix II, which includes titles of papers, should be of considerable assistance in this regard.

In this chapter we shall be concerned with a general approach to the kinds of data usually obtained and the methods used to arrive at useful results. Although gas chromatography is primarily a qualitative and quantitative analytical technique, this by no means exhausts the scope of the method. In addition, gas chromatography offers many possibilities for studying properties of solutions, the thermodynamics and mechanisms of adsorption and absorption, and the properties of surfaces.

GAS CHROMATOGRAPHIC DATA

Information from the Detector. Although it is customary to record the detector signal with a recording potentiometer, certain integral detectors do not require a recorder. For example, if carbon dioxide is used as a carrier gas, a gas collecting buret filled with potassium hydroxide solution serves as the detector and it is necessary to read the buret only at intervals. Even with a differential detector,

135

a very few carefully selected observations of the detector
response may serve the purpose for specific routine applications. In general, however, it is necessary to follow the
detector response continuously over a period of time and the
attenuated or amplified signal is recorded on a strip chart
recorder.

The only data obtained from the chromatograph is
a recording of detector signal versus time. For many purposes the time is a convenient variable. If the flow rate is
known and constant, the time can be easily converted to volume of carrier gas passed through the system. On the other
hand, the detector signal (position of the recorder pen) is
seldom a simple function of concentration of a component in
the carrier gas. Various methods of interpreting the signal
in order to obtain quantitative results will be considered.

Other Information. The amount of additional information required varies with the detector, the method of
obtaining analytical results, and the nature and accuracy of
the results expected. It may be necessary to obtain any or
all of the following information: nature of column packing,
type and amount of liquid phase, density of liquid phase,
nature of carrier gas, inlet and outlet pressures, flow rate,
column and detector temperatures, volume of dead space in
various parts of the system, interstitial volume in the column, and perhaps the history of the particular column.

QUALITATIVE ANALYSIS

Gas chromatography is primarily a method for
performing separations. Provided that the separation is
satisfactory, any suitable method can be used to identify the
pure components emerging from the column. Martin (456)
has suggested that the gas chromatograph might perform
preliminary separations and then, acting as a master control, send fractions out to other slave machines for detailed
analysis. This is not a simple problem because only small
samples are used and the components are highly diluted with
carrier gas. Infrared and mass spectroscopy have often
been used for identification. The method then loses the advantage of simplicity and low cost. Other methods such as
radioactivity may be applicable in special cases. For many

substances the human nose is an excellent and extremely
sensitive detector. A number of techniques for obtaining
identification from chromatographic information alone will
be considered next.

Use of Standards. In this method, the retention
times (or volumes) of the unknown peaks are compared with
the retention times of known pure compounds. The experimental conditions must be identical or appropriate correc-
tions applied. Alternatively, a known compound suspected
to be present in the unknown can be added to the sample.
The chromatograms taken before and after the addition are
compared for the presence of a new peak or the enhancement
of one already present. Identical retention times are not
proof of the identity of two substances unless the behavior
can be reproduced with a number of different column materials at different temperatures. Furthermore, while this
technique is simple in principle, it requires some knowledge
of the possible constituents and a large collection of pure
samples.
        The use of partition coefficients or specific reten-
tion volumes eliminates the requirement that the knowns and
unknowns be run under the same conditions. These properties depend only on the nature of the component, the column
material and the column temperature. Therefore literature
values can be used with any apparatus and only the temperature must be reproduced. Unfortunately only a limited
amount of such data is readily available. We can hope that
extensive tables will be collected and published, in fact the
JOURNAL OF CHROMATOGRAPHY is now including Tables
of Retention Volumes as a regular feature.

Retention Volume Plots. It is frequently possible
to separate components by class either by gas chromatography or preliminary chemical methods. Within a homologous series, retention time increases with molecular weight.
For many series a plot of the log retention volume versus
number of carbon atoms yields a straight line, excluding the
lowest members of the series. Data plotted in this form, as
shown in Fig. 13-1, are valuable in identifying unknown components. A few members of the series establish the relationship which can then be extended to cover the remaining homo-

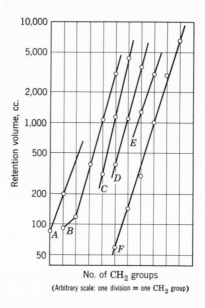

Fig. 13-1. Retention volume against number of carbon
atoms on a column of dinonyl phthalate.
Courtesy of Journal of Applied Chemistry (98).

A.   Paraffins, $n-C_5H_{12}$ – $n-C_7H_{16}$

B.   Alcohols (normal), CH_3OH – $n-C_5H_{11}OH$

C.   Formates, $HCO_2C_2H_5$ – $HCO_2C_4H_9$

D.   Acetates, $CH_3CO_2CH_3$ – $CH_3CO_2C_3H_7$

E.   Propionates, $C_2H_5CO_2CH_3$ – $C_2H_5CO_2C_2H_5$

F.   Methyl ketones, CH_3CHO – $n-C_5H_{11}COCH_3$

logues within reasonable limits.
        In Fig. 13-1 a retention volume of 1000 cc corre-
sponds to several compounds of differing numbers of carbon
atoms in the several series plotted. Unless the compound
can otherwise be classed in a definite series or its carbon
number determined independently, the identification from

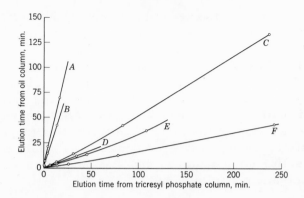

Fig. 13-2. Linear relation of retention times. Courtesy of
Analytical Chemistry (263).   A. Alkanes,
B. Cycloalkanes, C. Esters, D. Aldehydes,
E. Ketones, F. Alcohols.

from the retention volume alone is ambiguous. In this event
it is necessary to use a second column with a different stationary phase, yielding another pattern of retention volumes
versus molecular weights. In order to facilitate comparison,
the retention volume on one column is plotted versus the

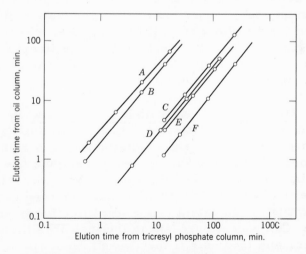

Fig. 13-3. Logarithmic relation of retention times. Cour-
tesy of Analytical Chemistry (263). A. Alkanes,
B. Cycloalkanes, C. Esters, D. Aldehydes,
E. Ketones, F. Alcohols.

retention volume on the second column. Fig. 13-2 is an example of this type of plot from which identification is reasonably certain. The slopes of the lines are characteristic of each class. The log-log plot shown in Fig. 13-3 is more convenient. Here the intercept is characteristic of the class. Obviously the more columns that are used, the more certain the identification. Desty and Whyman (368) have reported extensive tables of relative retention volumes (n-pentane = 1) for paraffins, aromatics, cyclopentanes, cyclohexanes, olefins and sulfur compounds on two stationary phases, n-hexatriacontane and benzyldiphenyl.

Multiple Detectors. Detector response is often considered to be the same for all components, or a correction factor is applied (vide infra). On the other hand, the variation in response can be used for identification. Consider two detectors, A and B, which have responses that are different functions of molecular weight. By connecting the two detectors in series at the end of the column, two signals are obtained for each component. One can plot the ratio of detector A response / detector B response versus molecular weight, and then use this curve to estimate the molecular weight of an unknown. Parameters other than molecular weight can be used; for example, the combination of thermal conductivity and radioactivity (579, 660). Perhaps the neatest arrangement of multiple detection is the flame ionization detector from which two independent signals can be obtained - both the flame temperature and an ion current.

Qualitative Identification of Mixtures. In a complicated chromatogram a pattern of peaks (including the peak heights) may help to identify a mixture which is a part of a more complex mixture. An interesting example has been reported by Schuck, Ford and Stephen (639), which in part was concerned with the identification of unburned gasoline in auto exhaust. The extent of the identification is shown in Fig. 13-4. Components present in the fuel were the only ones considered, and then only if they were present in the exhaust at a detectable level. Concentrations of the compounds of interest were then calculated on a molar basis (average of 17 experiments) and normalized for the fuel and the exhaust gas. From the comparison in Fig. 13-4, it is an obvious,

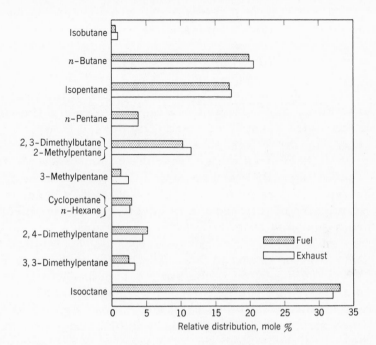

Fig. 13-4. Distribution of certain hydrocarbons in paraffinic fuel and in paraffinic exhaust-air mixtures. Compounds listed = 100%. Courtesy of Air Pollution Foundation (639).

but not necessarily correct, conclusion that there is unburned gasoline in auto exhaust. Some of the discrepancies are beyond experimental error; however, after the cracking process inside the engine, the comparison is surprisingly good.

Identification of Solvent. Just as the retention volumes from an array of solvents can establish the identity of a compound, in the same manner the retention volumes for an array of solutes can identify the solvent. A cleverly composited sample containing a variety of types of components will yield a chromatogram with a peak distribution which is characteristic of the solvent. Mackay (615) has used this technique to identify certain commercial polyoxyethylene derivatives of sorbitan and related compounds using a standard mixture of solutes consisting of esters and alcohols. Such a procedure is obviously cumbersome. How-

ever, with the advent of capillary columns which can be readily coated the method becomes more attractive.

QUANTITATIVE ANALYSIS

Integral Detectors. The response of integral detectors, e. g. , gas collected in a buret, volume delivered by
an autotitrator, quantity of electricity passed through a cou-
lometer, is a direct measure of the total amount of components which have been eluted from the column. Simple factors converting milliliters of gas, milliliters of titrant, cou-
lombs, etc. , to grams of sample are all that is necessary.
The remainder of this section is devoted to the interpretation
of chromatograms from differential detectors.

Use of Peak Heights. The height of the peak measured from the base line is the simplest method of quantitative analysis. For routine or control analysis where only a
few components must be determined, measurements at pre-
set times may supply the necessary information without taking the entire chromatogram. The method is extremely rapid so that it is easy to calibrate the instrument often. If the
method is used for process control, a calibration may be
programmed after every analysis.
The peak height versus concentration relationship
is linear over a limited range of concentration and varies
for each component as well as for each column and the operating conditions. Peak heights are most satisfactory for
components emerging from the column early where tall, narrow peaks are observed and are less satisfactory for components having long retention times and consequently low,
broad peaks. They are advantageous whenever highest accuracy is not essential or is too much of a luxury.

Use of Peak Areas. For a linear chromatographic
instrument, the peak area is proportional to the amount of
substance present. The proportionality constant depends on
the nature of the substance, the type of detector, and whether the amount is expressed on a weight or molar basis. For
thermal conductivity detectors, peak areas are also inversely proportional to the flow rate, but are otherwise independent of operating conditions providing only that the detector

temperature is constant. The thermal conductivity detector signal is not a simple function of concentration expressed either in weight per cent or mole per cent. If weight per cent is used, it is possible to obtain accurate results by applying a correction factor which is closely related to the thermal conductivity of the particular component. An extensive study of these factors has been reported by Messner, Rosie and Argabright (686), who found that the relative response (area per mole of component / area per mole of standard substance) of thermal conductivity detectors can be predicted from the molecular weight and class of the compound. They claim that the relative response is independent of the individual sensing unit (filament or thermistor), flow rate, concentration, and detector operating temperature. Extensive tables are given.

      For other types of detectors, the response will depend on other factors. The response of the beta-ray detector is primarily a function of weight per cent (hydrogen carrier gas) or molecular weight (argon carrier gas). The gas density balance responds to molecular weight. The introduction of a combustor prior to the detector provides a signal which depends on the molecular composition of the components. The response of the flame temperature detector depends on the heat of combustion.

      From the above discussion, it should be clear that indiscriminate use of peak areas as a measure of concentration is subject to serious errors. Calibration and correction factors must be applied according to the expected accuracy of the results.

      Internal Normalization of Peak Areas. In this method it is assumed that the total area under a chromatogram represents all of the sample components. The area under each peak is multiplied by the proper correction factor to convert it to grams or moles. The corrected area of a component divided by the total of the corrected areas for all components yields the fraction of each present in the sample. The accuracy of the analysis does not depend on accurate knowledge of the sample size. On the other hand the method does require a complete chromatogram, correction factors and much patience. For rough analysis, the correction factors are often assumed equal to unity with the consequent danger that more credence will be given to the result than it deserves.

If only a few components in the sample are of interest, the method can be abridged using only the area for those components normalized to 1 or 100. In this manner a relative distribution is obtained but not an absolute analysis.

Internal Standardization. In this method a known amount of a standard substance is added to a known volume of sample before it is chromatographed. Thus the concentration of the standard is known. The selection of the standard is important. It should be one that is inert toward all sample components, its peak should be readily and completely resolved from all others, and it should have a retention time intermediate to that of other components. To obtain the concentration of a component it is only necessary to multiply the concentration of the standard by the corrected area for the component and divide by the corrected area for the standard.

The standard substance may be added to the unknown mixture prior to sampling so that the sampling need not be accurate. This method is not limited to peak areas; peak heights may be used as well although calibration factors are imperative.

Measurement of Peak Areas. In many cases, the physical measurement of the peak area is the limiting factor in the accuracy of the results. A number of methods have been proposed.

1.   Cut out the peak with a scissors and weigh the paper. This is very inexpensive but tedious. The accuracy is limited by the patience of the operator and the uniformity of the paper.

2.   Measure the area with a planimeter. This is a more elegant instrument than a scissors and is relatively inexpensive, but again is limited by the patience of the operator. It is impractical for routine analysis where miles of chart paper may be involved.

3.   Multiply the peak height by the peak width at half height. For symmetric peaks this simple method is equally as accurate as the more tedious methods of measuring area. However, peaks with lead-

ing or tailing edges are not suitable.

4. Multiply the peak height by the retention time. The peak width (as well as the width at half height) is directly proportional to retention time and the peak height is inversely proportional to retention time. Therefore, areas determined in this fashion can be treated in the same manner as the actual areas under the peaks.

5. Use an automatic integrator. Several integrators are now available commercially as accessories to standard recorders. (See Chapter 12). The area enclosed by the chromatographic trace is given by a secondary pipping pen or a digital read-out device. Some are designed to record the sub-total area each time the pen returns to the base line, but as yet the problem of overlapping peaks is still left to the operator.

Overlapping Peaks. When either peak areas or peak heights are used, difficulties arise if the components are not completely separated, resulting in overlapping peaks. If accurate results are required, it may be well to look for another stationary phase with a greater resolving power or to collect the unresolved material for further treatment.

Brace (671) has made an interesting study of the quantitative evaluation of overlapping peaks. He used an ingenious simplification which, however, is valid for other cases. The sample was a blend of benzene, toluene and p-xylene in a ratio of 2:3:5 - chosen because all peaks were approximately the same height. A conventional analysis gave three completely resolved peaks. Incomplete resolution was simulated by the successive addition of two samples with a variable time delay between injections. Thus two adjacent peaks were obtained for each of the three components. The degree of resolution between any two peaks for the same component was increased by increasing the time delay. Peak heights were varied by changing the ratio of the sample sizes. Peak widths were changed by varying the flow rate and temperature.

In all cases the two benzene peaks were well resolved permitting a determination of the peak ratios that should be obtained for the partially resolved p-xylene peaks.

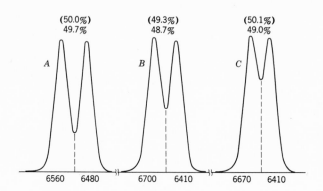

Fig. 13-5. Incomplete resolution of peaks with similar peak
heights. After Brace (671).

All data given refer to the latter peaks. Areas were measured with an integrator attachment made by the Disc Instrument Company.

Fig. 13-5 shows three degrees of non-resolution.
Below each pair of peaks is the integrated area using the
minimum between the peaks as a dividing line. The values
above the peaks are the peak ratios (area of the peak / total
area of both peaks) using the integrated values. In parenthe-

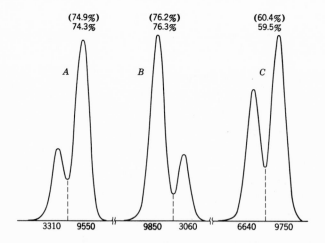

Fig. 13-6. Incomplete resolution of peaks with different
peak heights. After Brace (671).

ses is the corresponding value determined from the completely resolved benzene peaks.

Fig. 13-6 shows the effect of different peak heights
produced by using two different sample sizes. The peak ratios have been determined as above, and again show adequate
agreement.

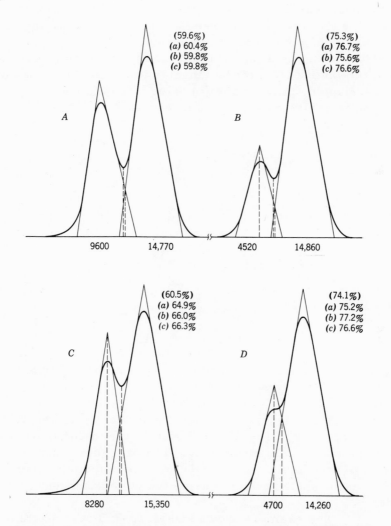

Fig. 13-7. Incomplete resolution of peaks of different
heights and widths. After Brace (671).

Broader peaks, simulated by changing the flow rate and temperature, result in still poorer resolution as shown in Fig. 13-7. Here the major peak in each pair has been evaluated by four techniques. The value in parentheses has been determined from the ratio of the benzene peaks and is assumed to be the correct value. The (a) value above each major peak was determined directly from the integrated values using the minimum between the peaks as a dividing line. The (b) value was determined from the "corrected" integrated values using as a dividing line the perpendicular dropped from the intersection of the tangents to the inside slopes of the overlapping peaks. The (c) value was obtained by approximating triangles as explained in Fig. 13-8.

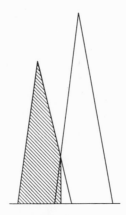

Fig. 13-8.   Resolution by method of approximating triangles. After Brace (671).

When non-resolution obviously distorts one of the inside slopes as in Fig. 13-7, B and C, the inside tangent would be completely misleading. The procedure then is to pass a perpendicular through the peak maximum and construct an isosceles triangle using the outside tangent as one side.

The example shown in Fig. 13-7 D is an extreme case of non-resolution and illustrates roughly the limitations of these techniques.

The method of approximating triangles can be applied whether or not there is peak overlap. Triangles are formed from the tangents or hypothetical tangents as shown in Fig. 13-8. The area corresponding to the first peak is shaded and the remaining area corresponds to the second peak. Each area divided by the total area gives the per cent composition. The total area enclosed by the triangles tends to be higher than that obtained from integration. From the limited amount of data available, the correction seems to be consistent and is of no concern if all data is obtained in the same manner.

Brace concludes that "the results of this investigation suggest that resolution must be very poor indeed in order to interfere seriously with quantitative results by gas chromatography."

From this limited study, we cannot conclude that this technique will give equally satisfactory results in all cases. An extreme case is shown in Fig. 13-9, where the peak of a trace amount (0.2%) of sec-butyl alcohol is masked by the trailing edge of the major component, isopropyl alcohol. The peak height is not a suitable measure of concentration, and the peak area is evidently determined by using an artificial base line drawn by continuing the isopropyl alcohol trace in a smooth curve. This technique was checked with known synthetic mixtures (439). A definitive study of the quantitative interpretation of overlapping peaks would be very valuable if general methods can be proved valid.

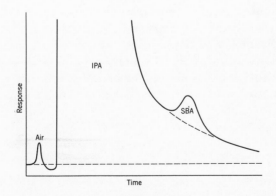

Fig. 13-9. Trace amount of secondary butyl alcohol (SBA) in crude isopropyl alcohol (IPA). Courtesy of Reinhold Publishing Corporation (439).

Quantitative Analysis of the Solvent. At a fixed
temperature and sample size, the retention time of a solute
is proportional to the weight of the solvent in the stationary
phase. Retention times, therefore, give some quantitative
information regarding the solvent.

Use of retention times to analyze a binary solvent
mixture is purely speculative at this stage, but with the field
moving so fast, what is speculation today may be an accomplished fact tomorrow. Consider the following rather use-
less example to illustrate the point. Acetone is much more
soluble in water than in glycerol, and there is little doubt
that the retention time of acetone would be greater for a
water stationary phase than for glycerol. It seems intuitive-
ly obvious that for a fixed weight of mixed solvent (water
plus glycerol) the retention time of acetone should increase
in a regular fashion as the ratio of water to glycerol is increased. Using two solutes, such as acetone and diethyl
ketone, it is probable that the ratio of retention times would
be a unique function of the composition of the liquid phase at
a given temperature. The retention time ratio has the obvious advantage that it does not depend on the manner of packing the column or other operational parameters.

Another case of perhaps greater interest is the
estimation of relative amounts of optical isomers. It will be
recalled that optical isomers are identical in all physical
properties for all operations that are symmetric. The physical properties can be different, and appreciably so, for un-
symmetric operations. Two optical isomers could conceivably be separated if they were sufficiently volatile, and if
the stationary phase was optically active or contained an
optically active substance. Conversely, a single member of
an optically active pair should have a retention time that
depended on the relative amounts of optical isomers com-
prising the solvent.

Appendix I

LIST OF
MANUFACTURERS

A. MANUFACTURERS OF GAS CHROMATOGRAPHS

American Instrument Company, 8030 Georgia Ave.,
Silver Spring, Maryland

Barber-Colman Company, Rockford, Illinois

Beckman, Scientific Instruments, Fullerton, California

Burrell Corporation, 2223 Fifth Ave., Pittsburgh 19,
Pennsylvania

Central Scientific Company, 1700 Irving Park Blvd.,
Chicago, Illinois

Consolidated Electrodynamics Corporation, 300 North
Sierra Madre Villa, Pasadena, California

Davis Instruments, 47 Halleck St., Newark 4, New Jersey

F and M Scientific Corporation, 1001 Kendall Rd.,
Wilmington 5, Delaware

Fisher Scientific Company, 711 Forbes Ave., Pittsburgh
19, Pennsylvania

Jarrell-Ash Company, 26 Farwell St., Newtonville 60,
Massachusetts

Leeds and Northrup, 4907 Stenton Ave., Philadelphia 44,
Pennsylvania

Loe Engineering Company, 237 North Fair Oaks Ave.,
Pasadena, California

Perkin-Elmer Corporation, Norwalk, Connecticut

Podbielniak, Incorporated, 341 East Ohio St., Chicago 11,
Illinois

Precision Scientific Company, 3737 West Cortland St.,
Chicago 47, Illinois
Research Specialties Company, 200 South Garrard Blvd.,
Richmond, California
Wilkens Instrument and Research, Incorporated, P.O. Box
313, Walnut Creek, California

B. OTHER COMPANIES MENTIONED IN TEXT

Barnes Engineering Company, 30 Commerce Rd.,
Stamford, Connecticut
Conoflow Corporation, 2012 Arch St., Philadelphia,
Pennsylvania
Disc Instrument Company, 12671 Bubbling Well Rd.,
Santa Ana, California
Fischer and Porter Company, Hatboro, Pennsylvania
Gow-Mac Instrument Company, 100 Kings Rd., Madison,
New Jersey
Johns-Manville Corporation, 22 East 40th St., New York
16, New York
Hamilton Company, 1134 Whitley St., Whittier, California
Hoke, Incorporated, 138 South Dean St., Englewood, New
Jersey
Linde Air Products Company, 30 East 42nd St., New York
17, New York
Victory Engineering Company, Springfield Rd., Union, New
Jersey

Appendix **II**

BIBLIOGRAPHY

1930

1. Peters, K. and Weil, K.   THE SEPARATION OF GASES BY ADSORPTION ON CHARCOAL.   Z. angew. Chem. 43, 608-12 (1930).

1933

2. Daynes, H. A.   GAS ANALYSIS BY MEASUREMENT OF THERMAL CONDUCTIVITY.   Cambridge University Press, London, 1933.

1936

3. Eucken, A. and Knick, H.   AUTOMATIC PROCEDURE FOR THE MICROANALYTICAL SEPARATION OF LOW-BOILING HYDROCARBONS BY DESORPTION, Brennstoff-Chem. 17, 241-44 (1936); C. A. 31, 1727 (1937).

1940

4. Wilson, J. N.   A THEORY OF CHROMATOGRAPHY. J. Am. Chem. Soc. 62, 1583-91 (1940).

1941

5. Martin, A. J. P. and Synge, R. L. M.   A NEW FORM OF CHROMATOGRAM EMPLOYING TWO LIQUID PHASES. I. A THEORY OF CHROMATOGRAPHY: II. APPLICATION OF THE MICRODETERMINATION OF THE HIGHER

MONOAMINOACIDS IN PROTEINS, Biochem. J. 35,
1358-68 (1941); C.A. 36, 5197(4) (1942).

1942

6. Coull, J., Engel, H. C. and Miller, J. A NEW TECH-
NIQUE FOR ADSORPTION STUDIES, Ind. Eng. Chem.,
Anal. Ed., 14, 459-62 (1942); C.A. 31, 4747(2) (1942).

7. Hesse, G. and Tschachotin, B. ADSORPTION ANALYSIS
OF GASES AND VAPORS, Naturwiss. 30, 387-92 (1942);
C.A. 37, 6211(3) (1943).

1943

8. DeVault, D. THE THEORY OF CHROMATOGRAPHY
J. Am. Chem. Soc. 65, 532-40 (1943).

9. Turner, N. C. THE ANALYSIS OF HYDROCARBON
GASES BY MEANS OF ADSORPTION FRACTIONATION,
Natl. Petrol News 35, R234-37 (1943); Petrol Refiner 22,
140-44(1943); C.A. 37, 3914(4) (1943).

1945

10. Brunauer, S. PHYSICAL ADSORPTION OF GASES AND
VAPOURS, Oxford University Press, 1945.

1946

11. Claesson, Stig. STUDIES ON ADSORPTION AND AD-
SORPTION ANALYSIS WITH SPECIAL REFERENCE TO
HOMOLOGOUS SERIES, Arkiv. Kemi,. Mineral, Geol.
23A (1), 1-133, (1946); C. A. 40, 3665 (1946).

12. Glueckauf, E. A MICROANALYSIS OF THE HELIUM
AND NEON CONTENTS OF AIR. Proc. Roy. Soc.
(London) A185, 98-119 (1946).

1947

13. Coates, J. I. and Glueckauf, E. THEORY OF CHRO-
MATOGRAPHY. III. EXPERIMENTAL SEPARATION
OF TWO SOLUTES AND COMPARISON WITH THEORY.
J. Chem. Soc. 1947, 1308-14.

14. Glueckauf, E. THEORY OF CHROMATOGRAPHY. II.
    CHROMATOGRAMS OF A SINGLE SOLUTE. J. Chem.
    Soc. 1947, 1302-08.

15. Glueckauf, E. and Coates, J.I., THEORY OF CHROMA-
    TOGRAPHY. IV. THE INFLUENCE IN INCOMPLETE
    EQUILIBRIUM ON THE FRONT BOUNDARY OF CHROMA-
    TOGRAMS AND ON THE EFFECTIVENESS OF SEPARA-
    TION, J. Chem. Soc. 1947, 1315-20.

16. Glueckauf, E. THEORY OF CHROMATOGRAPHY. V.
    SEPARATION OF TWO SOLUTES FOLLOWING A
    FREUNDLICH ISOTHERM, J. Chem. Soc. 1947, 1321-29.

17. Martin, A.J.P. THE PRINCIPLES OF CHROMATOG-
    RAPHY. Endeavour 6, 21-28 (1947).

18. Mayer, S. W. and Tompkins. A THEORETICAL ANALY-
    SIS OF THE COLUMN SEPARATIONS PROCESS. J. Am.
    Chem. Soc. 69, 2866-74 (1947).

                        1949

19. Claesson, S. THEORY OF FRONTAL ANALYSIS AND
    DISPLACEMENT DEVELOPMENT, Discussions Faraday
    Soc. 7, 34-38 (1949).

20. Claesson, S. CHROMATOGRAPHIC ANALYSIS. HIGH
    MOLECULAR POLYMER SEPARATION, Discussions
    Faraday Soc., 7, 321-25 (1949).

21. Glueckauf, E. THEORY OF CHROMATOGRAPHY. VI.
    PRECISION MEASUREMENTS OF ADSORPTION AND
    EXCHANGE ISOTHERMS FROM COLUMN-ELUTION
    DATA, J. Chem. Soc. 1949, 3280-85.

22. Glueckauf, E. THEORY OF CHROMATOGRAPHY. VII.
    THE GENERAL THEORY OF TWO SOLUTES FOLLOWING
    NON-LINEAR ISOTHERMS, Discussions Faraday Soc. 7,
    12-25 (1949).

23. Glueckauf, E., Barker, K.N. and Kitt, G.P. THEORY
    OF CHROMATOGRAPHY. VIII. THE SEPARATION OF
    LITHIUM ISOTOPES BY ION EXCHANGE AND OF NEON
    ISOTOPES BY LOW TEMPERATURE ADSORPTION

COLUMNS, Discussions Faraday Soc. , 7, 193-213 (1949).

24. Kofler, W. SEPARATION AND PURIFICATION OF OR-
GANIC COMPOUNDS BY MEANS OF SUBLIMATION
THROUGH ADSORPTIVE SUBSTANCES, Monatsh. Chem.,
80, 694-701 (1949); C. A. 44, 3407 (1950).

25. Phillips, C. S. G. THE CHROMATOGRAPHY OF GASES
AND VAPOURS, Discussions Faraday Soc. , 1949, 241-48;
C. A. 45, 1460e (1951).

26. Turkeltaub, N. M. CHROMATOGRAPHIC TITRIMETRIC
GAS ANALYZER, Zavodskaya Lab. 15, 653-60 (1949);
C. A. 44, 9747e (1950).

1950

27. Russell, A. S. and Cochrane, C. N. SURFACE AREAS OF
HEATED ALUMINA HYDRATES. Ind. Eng. Chem. 42,
1336-40 (1950).

28. Turkeltaub, N. M. CHROMATOGRAPHIC METHOD FOR
SEPARATE DETERMINATION OF MICROCONCENTRA-
TION OF HYDROCARBONS IN AIR, Zhur. Anal. Khim. 5,
200-10 (1950).

1951

29. Cassidy, H. G. ADSORPTION AND CHROMATOGRAPHY,
Interscience Publishers, Inc. , New York (1951).

30. Cremer, E. and Prior, F. APPLICATION OF CHROMA-
TOGRAPHIC METHODS TO THE SEPARATION OF GASES
AND DETERMINATION OF ADSORPTION ENERGIES,
Z. Elektrochem. 55, 66-70 (1951); C. A. 45, 9334h (1951).

31. Cremer, E. and Müller, R. SEPARATION AND DETER-
MINATION OF SUBSTANCES BY CHROMATOGRAPHY IN
THE GAS PHASE, Z. Elektrochem. 55, 217-20 (1951);
C. A. 45, 9335a (1951).

32. Cremer, E. and Müller, R. SEPARATION AND DETER-
MINATION OF SMALL QUANTITIES OF GASES BY CHRO-
MATOGRAPHY, Mikrochemie ver. Mikrochim. Acta 36/37,
553-560 (1951); C. A. 46, 5057h (1951).

33. Hammar, C.C.B. A SIMPLE APPARATUS FOR ADSORP-
TION ANALYSIS OF GASES, Svensk. Kem. Tidskr. 63,
125-35 (1951) in English; C.A. 45, 10551g (1951).

34. Herzfeld, K.F. and Smallwood, H.M. Chapter 1 in
Taylor, H.S. and Glasstone, S. TREATISE ON PHYSICAL
CHEMISTRY, Vol. 2, 3rd Ed. D. Van Nostrand Co. New
York 1951.

35. Hesse, G. THE RATE FACTOR OF ADSORPTION PRO-
CESSES IN CHROMATOGRAPHIC COLUMNS, Z. Elektrochem. 55, 60-65 (1951); C.A. 45, 9335b (1951).

36. Lenoir, J.M. and Comings, E.W. THERMAL CONDUC-
TIVITY OF GASES - MEASUREMENT AT HIGH PRES-
SURE, Chem. Eng. Progress 47, 223-31 (1951).

37. Minter, C.C. and Burdy, L.M.J. THERMAL CONDUC-
TIVITY BRIDGE FOR GAS ANALYSIS, Anal. Chem. 23,
143-47 (1951).

38. Phillips, G. AN ELECTRONIC METHOD OF DETECTING
IMPURITIES IN THE AIR, J. Sci. Instr. 28, 342-47(1951).

39. Weaver, E.R. GAS ANALYSIS BY METHODS DEPENDING
ON THERMAL CONDUCTIVITY, Berl, W.G., Ed.,
"Physical Methods in Chemical Analysis", Vol. II,
Academic Press, Inc., New York 1951, pp. 387-437.

40. Zhukhovitskii, A.A., Zolotareva, O.V., Sokolov, V.A.
and Turkeltaub, N.M. NEW METHOD OF CHROMATOG-
RAPHIC ANALYSIS. Doklady Akad, Nauk S.S.S.R. 77,
435-38 (1951).

1952

41. El-Shazly, K. DEGRADATION OF PROTEIN IN THE
RUMEN OF SHEEP, Biochem J. 51, 640-53 (1952).

42. Griffiths, J., James, D. and Phillips, C., GAS CHRO-
MATOGRAPHY, Analyst 77, 897-904 (1952); C.A. 47,
1530b (1953).

43. James, A.T. GAS-LIQUID PARTITION CHROMATOG-
RAPHY. THE SEPARATION OF VOLATILE ALIPHATIC

AMINES AND OF HOMOLOGUES OF PYRIDINE, Biochem.
J. 52, 242-47 (1952); C.A. 47, 446b (1953).

44. James, A. T. and Martin, A. J. P. GAS-LIQUID PARTI-
TION CHROMATOGRAPHY: THE SEPARATION AND
MICRO-ESTIMATION OF VOLATILE FATTY ACIDS
FROM FORMIC ACID TO DODECANOIC ACID, J. Bio-
chem. 50, 679-90 (1952); C.A. 46, 4883i (1952).

45. James, A. T. and Martin, A. J. P. GAS-LIQUID PARTI-
TION CHROMATOGRAPHY. A TECHNIQUE FOR THE
ANALYSIS OF VOLATILE MATERIALS, Analyst 77, 915-
932 (1952); C.A. 47, 1529d (1953).

46. James, A. T. and Martin, A. J. P. GAS-LIQUID PARTI-
TION CHROMATOGRAPHY. THE SEPARATION AND
MICRO-ESTIMATION OF VOLATILE FATTY ACIDS AND
BASES. Congr. intern. biochim. 2^e Congr., Paris, 1952;
C.A. 49, 12082 (1955).

47. James, A. T., Martin, A. J. P. and Smith, G. H. GAS-
LIQUID PARTITION CHROMATOGRAPHY. THE SEPA-
RATION AND MICRO-ESTIMATION OF AMMONIA AND
THE METHYLAMINES, Biochem. J. 52, 238-42 (1952);
C.A. 47, 446d (1953).

48. James, D. H. and Phillips, C.S.G. A SIMPLE GAS-
FLOW CONTROL OF HIGH EFFICIENCY. J. Sci. Instr.
29, 362-63 (1952); C.A., 47, 3048 (1953).

49. Klima, J. METHODS OF GAS ANALYSIS. Paliva 32,
275-82 (1952); C.A., 50, 8391 (1956).

50. Martin, A. J. P. DEVELOPMENT OF PARTITION
CHROMATOGRAPHY. Prix Nobel 1952, 110-21.

51. Pritchard, F.W. and Walton, W. H. A NEW TECHNIQUE
OF GAS SAMPLING, Chem. & Ind.(London) 1952, 166.

52. Pritchard, F.W. MODIFIED THERMAL CONDUCTIVITY
GAS ANALYZER FOR MEASURING METHANE IN AIR OR
CARBON DIOXIDE, J. Sci. Instr. 29, 116-17 (1952); C.A.
46, 5898a (1952).

53. Synge, R. L. M. APPLICATIONS OF PARTITION CHRO-

MATOGRAPHY. Prix Nobel 1952, 122-35.

54. Williams, R. J. P. GRADIENT ELUTION ANALYSIS,
    Analyst 77, 915 (1952).

55. Wirth, H. QUALITATIVE AND QUANTITATIVE MICRO-
    GAS-ANALYSIS BY THE DESORPTION-HEAT-CONDUC-
    TIVITY METHOD, Mikrochemie ver Mikrochim. Acta 40,
    15-20 (1952); C. A. 47, 993g (1953).

                          1953

56. Aivazov, B. V. and Vyakhirev, D. A. SEPARATION OF A
    MIXTURE OF SIMPLEST HYDROCARBONS BY THE
    METHOD OF CHROMATOGRAPHY, Zhur. Priklad. Khim.
    26, 505-11 (1953); C. A. 48, 6371h (1954).

57. Barrer, R. M. and Robins, A. B. SORPTION OF MIX-
    TURES. PART I. MOLECULAR SIEVES SEPARATION
    OF PERMANENT AND INERT GASES, Trans. Faraday
    Soc. 49, 807-15 (1953); C. A. 48, 3099h (1954).

58. Cropper, F. R. and Heywood, A. ANALYTICAL SEPA-
    RATION OF THE METHYLESTERS OF THE $C_{12} - C_{22}$
    FATTY ACIDS BY VAPOUR-PHASE CHROMATOGRAPHY,
    Nature 172, 1101-02 (1953); C. A. 48, 3203c (1954).

59. Guild, L. V. THE ANALYSIS OF LIGHT HYDROCARBON
    GASES BY FRACTIONAL ADSORPTION, Proceedings
    32nd Ann. Convention Natural Gasoline Assoc. of America
    (1953).

60. Irving, H. M. N. H. and Williams, R. J. P. PARTITION
    CHROMATOGRAPHY, Sci. Progr. 41, 418-32 (1953);
    C. A. 47, 8460c (1953).

61. James, D. H. and Phillips, C. S. G. THE CHROMATOG-
    RAPHY OF GASES AND VAPOURS. PART II., J. Chem.
    Soc. 1953, 1600-10; C. A. 47, 9861d (1953).

62. Janak, J. SEMI-MICROANALYSIS OF GASES. Collection
    Czechoslov. Chem. Communs. 18, 798 (1953).

63. Janak, J. CHROMATOGRAPHIC SEMI-MICROANALYSIS
    OF GASES, Chem. listy 47, 464-67 (1953); C. A. 48, 3196h
    (1954).

64. Janak, J. CHROMATOGRAPHIC SEMI-MICROANALYSIS OF GASES. I. THEORY AND METHOD OF ANALYSIS, Chem. listy 47, 817-27 (1953); C.A. 48, 3197a (1954); Collection Czechoslov. Chem. Communs. 19, 684-99(1954).

65. Janak, J. CHROMATOGRAPHIC SEMI-MICROANALYSIS OF GASES. II. ANALYSIS OF NATURAL GAS AND DE-TERMINATION OF METHANE IN MINE GASES. Chem. listy 47, 828-36 (1953); C.A. 48, 3197b (1954); Collection Czechoslov. Chem. Communs. 19, 684-99 (1954).

66. Janak, J. CHROMATOGRAPHIC SEMI-MICROANALYSIS OF GASES. III. ANALYSIS OF HYDROGEN GASES, Chem. listy 47, 837-41 (1953); C.A. 48, 3197c (1954); Collection Czechoslov. Chem. Communs. 19, 684-99 (1954).

67. Janak, J. CHROMATOGRAPHIC SEMI-MICROANALYSIS OF GASES. IV. ANALYSIS OF GASEOUS PARAFFINS, Chem. listy 47, 1184-89 (1953); C.A. 48, 3853f (1954); Collection Czechoslov. Chem. Communs. 19, 700 (1954).

68. Janak, J. and Rusek, M. CHROMATOGRAPHIC SEMI-MICROANALYSIS OF GASES. V. ANALYSIS OF UNSAT-URATED C_2 AND C_3 HYDROCARBONS, Chem. listy 47, 1190-96 (1953); C.A. 48, 3853g (1954); Collection Czechoslov. Chem. Communs. 19, 700-11(1954).

69. Janak, J. CHROMATOGRAPHIC SEMI-MICROANALYSIS OF GASES. VI. ANALYSIS OF RARE GASES, Chem. listy 47, 1348-53 (1953); C.A. 48, 3854b (1954); Collection Czechoslov. Chem. Communs. 19, 917-24 (1954).

70. Janak, J. and Paralova, I. CHROMATOGRAPHIC SEMI-MICROANALYSIS OF GASES. VII. ANALYSIS OF DIS-SOLVED GASES, Chem. listy 47, 1476-80 (1953); C.A. 48, 3854c (1954); Collection Czechoslov. Chem. Communs. 20, 336-41 (1955).

71. Mignolet, J.C.P. SIMPLE AND MULTIPLE GAS MICRO-INTRODUCERS FOR ADSORPTION STUDIES. J. Sci. Instr. 30, 15-17 (1953).

72. Takahashi, A. AUTOMATIC CONTINUOUS MEASURE-MENT OF MINUTE AMOUNTS OF GASES BY THE ELEC-TRIC CONDUCTIVITY METHOD, Kagaku no Ryoiki

(J. Japan. Chem.) 77, 783-88 (1953); C.A. 48, 13536h
(1954).

73. Turkeltaub, N.M., Shvartsman, V.P., Georgievskaya,
T.V., Zolotareva, O.V., and Karymova, A.I.
SEPARATION OF HYDROCARBON MIXTURES BY THE
CHROMATHERMOGRAPHIC METHOD, Zhur. Fiz. Khim.
27, 1827-36 (1953); C.A. 48, 10476e (1954).

74. Vyakhirev, D.A., Bruk, A.I. and Guglina, S.A.
VOLUMETRIC-CHROMATOGRAPHIC METHOD OF GAS
ANALYSIS, Doklady Akad. Nauk S.S.S.R. 90, 577-9 (1953).

75. Williams, T. I. THE ELEMENTS OF CHROMATOG-
RAPHY, Philosophical Library, Inc., New York (1953).

76. Wirth, H. THE SEPARATION OF GASES BY SORPTION
PROCESSES, Monatsh. Chem. 84, 156-68 (1953); C.A.
47, 7285a (1953).

77. Wirth, H. THE SEPARATION OF GASES BY SORPTION
PROCESSES. II., Monatsh. Chem. 84, 741-50 (1953);
C.A. 48, 2440d (1954).

78. Wormser, E.M. PROPERTIES OF THERMISTOR INFRA-
RED DETECTORS. J. Opt. Soc. Am. 43, 15-21 (1953).

79. Zhukhovitskii, A.A., Turkeltaub, N.M. and Sokolov, V.A.
THEORY OF CHROMATHERMOGRAPHY, Doklady Akad.
Nauk. S.S.S.R. 88, 859-62 (1953); C.A. 47, 11882d (1953).

80. Zhukhovitskii, A.A., Turkeltaub, N.M. and Georgievskaya,
T.V. CONTINUOUS CHROMATOGRAPHY, Doklady Akad.
Nauk S.S.S.R. 92, 987-90 (1953).

1954

81. Berridge, N.J. and Watts, J.D. SEPARATION OF MIX-
TURES OF METHYL KETONES. J. Sci. Food Agr. 5,
417-21 (1954); C.A. 49, 783 (1955).

82. Clayton, R.A. and Strong, F.M. PARTITION CHROMA-
TOGRAPHY OF A HOMOLOGOUS SERIES OF VOLATILE
PRIMARY AMINES, Anal. Chem. 26, 579-80 (1954).

83. Cropper, F. R. and Heywood, A. IMPROVEMENTS IN VAPOUR-PHASE CHROMATOGRAPHY AT RELATIVELY HIGH TEMPERATURES, Nature 174, 1063-64 (1954); C. A. 49, 5197f (1955).

84. Davison, W. H. T. , Slaney, S. and Wragg, A. L. NOVEL METHOD OF IDENTIFICATION OF POLYMERS, Chem. & Ind. (London) 1954, 1356; C. A. 49, 3736i (1955).

85. Griffiths, J. H. and Phillips, C. S. G. THE CHROMATOGRAPHY OF GASES AND VAPOURS. IV. APPLICATIONS OF THE SURFACE-POTENTIAL DETECTOR, J. Chem. Soc. 1954, 3446-53; C. A. 49, 2125i (1955).

86. Guild, L. V. THE ANALYSIS OF LP GASES BY FRACTIONAL ADSORPTION, Presented at Symp. on Methods for Testing Liquefied Pet. Gases, St. Louis, Mo. , Sept. 1954.

87. Hansen, R. P. and McInnes, A. G. VOLATILE ACIDS OF OX PERINEPHRIC FAT. Nature 173, 1093 (1954).

88. James, A. T. CHROMATOGRAPHY, Brit. Med. Bull. (Special issue) Vol. 10, No. 3, 165 (1954).

89. James, A. T. and Martin, A. J. P. GAS-LIQUID CHROMATOGRAPHY. A TECHNIQUE FOR THE ANALYSIS AND IDENTIFICATION OF VOLATILE MATERIALS, Brit. Med. Bull. 10, 170-76 (1954) C. A. 49, 9428b (1955).

90. James, D. H. and Phillips, C. S. G. THE CHROMATOGRAPHY OF GASES AND VAPOURS. III. THE DETERMINATION OF ADSORPTION ISOTHERMS, J. Chem. Soc. 1954, 1066-1070; C. A. 48, 7958g (1954).

91. Janak, J. and Rusek, M. CHROMATOGRAPHIC SEMI-MICROANALYSIS OF GASES. VIII. SEPARATION AND ANALYSIS OF SOME HALOGENATED HYDROCARBONS, Chem. listy 48, 207-11 (1954); C. A. 48, 6321f (1954).

92. Janak, J. and Rusek, M. CHROMATOGRAPHIC SEMI-MICROANALYSIS OF GASES. IX. DETERMINATION OF NITROUS OXIDE, Chem. listy 48, 397-400 (1954); C. A. 48, 7489f (1954); Collection Czechoslov. Chem. Communs. 20, 343-47 (1955).

93. Janak, J. and Tesarik, K. CHROMATOGRAPHIC SEMI-
MICROANALYSIS OF GASES. X. DETERMINATION OF
SMALL AND TRACE AMOUNTS OF HELIUM, NEON, AND
HYDROGEN IN GASES, Chem. listy 48, 397-400 (1954);
C. A. 48, 13536 (1954); Collection Czechoslov. Chem.
Communs., 20, 348-55 (1955).

94. Jordan, T. E. THE VAPOR PRESSURE OF ORGANIC
COMPOUNDS. Interscience Publishers, New York, 1954.

95. Knight, H. S. and Groennings INDICATOR CHROMATOG-
RAPHIC ANALYSIS OF ORGANIC MIXTURES. Anal.
Chem. 26, 1549 (1954).

96. Martin, A. J. P. CHROMATOGRAPHY INTRODUCTION,
Brit. Med. Bull. 10, 161-62 (1954).

97. Pollard, F. H., Pedler, A. E. and Hardy, C. J. EFFECT
OF NITROGEN DIOXIDE ON THE THERMAL DECOMPO-
SITION OF ETHYL NITRITE. Nature 174, 979 (1954).

98. Ray, N. H. GAS CHROMATOGRAPHY. I. THE SEPA-
RATION AND ESTIMATION OF VOLATILE ORGANIC
COMPOUNDS BY GAS-LIQUID PARTITION CHROMATOG-
RAPHY, J. Appl. Chem. 4, 21 (1954); C. A. 49, 2257 (1955).

99. Ray, N. H. GAS CHROMATOGRAPHY. II. THE SEPA-
RATION AND ANALYSIS OF GAS MIXTURES BY CHRO-
MATOGRAPHIC METHODS, J. Appl. Chem. 4, 82-85
(1954); C. A. 48, 11244d (1954).

100. Spengler, G. and Wallner, E. ADSORPTIVE TRENNUNG
VON WACHSEN UND WACHSKOMPONENTEN, Fette Seifen
Anstrickmittel 56, Jahrgang Nr. 10, (1954).

101. Tenney, H. M. and Sturgis, F. E. SEPARABILITY OF
HYDROCARBONS BY ELUTION CHROMATOGRAPHY,
Anal. Chem. 26, 946-53 (1954).

102. Turkeltaub, N. M. NEW ADSORPTION METHODS OF
ANALYSIS OF HYDROCARBON GASES, Neflyanoe Khoz.
32, (4), 72-77 (1954); C. A. 48, 8517f (1954).

103. de Verdier, C. H. and Sjöberg, C. I. AN AUTOMATIC
CONDUCTIVITY BRIDGE FOR CHROMATOGRAPHIC

ANALYSES, Acta Chem.Scand. 8, 1161-68 (1954); C. A. 49, 8633g (1955).

104. Williams, R. J. P. GENERAL PRINCIPLES OF CHROMA-
TOGRAPHY, Brit. Med. Bull. 10, 165-69 (1954).

105. Wilson, J. E. A SENSITIVE VERSATILE ACOUSTIC GAS
ANALYZER PARTICULARLY SUITABLE FOR THE
ANALYSIS OF ANESTHETIC MIXTURES, Rev. Sci. Instr.
25, 927-28, (1954).

1955

106. Allen, R. R. CHROMATOGRAPHY, J. Am. Oil Chem.
Soc. 32, 638-40 (1955).

107. Ambrose, D. A. and Collerson, R. R.   A THERMAL
CONDUCTIVITY GAUGE FOR USE IN GAS-LIQUID PARTI-
TION CHROMATOGRAPHY, J. Sci. Instr. 32, 323 (1955).

108. Barefoot, R. R. and Currah, J. E. VAPOUR-PHASE
CHROMATOGRAPHY, Chem. in Can. 7, (11), 45-48, 50,
52 (1955); C. A. 50, 3143f (1956).

109. Blom, L. and Edelhausen, L. DIRECT TITRATION OF
CARBON DIOXIDE. Anal. Chim. Acta 13, 120-28 (1955).

110. Bradford, B. W., Harvey, D. and Chalkley, D. E., THE
CHROMATOGRAPHIC ANALYSIS OF HYDROCARBON
MIXTURES, J. Inst. Petrol. 41, 80-91 (1955); C. A. 49,
7839h (1955).

111. Callear, A. B. and Cvetanovic, R. J. THE APPLICATION
OF GAS-LIQUID PARTITION CHROMATOGRAPHY TO
PROBLEMS IN CHEMICAL KINETICS, Can. J. Chem. 33,
1256-67 (1955); C. A. 49, 14421i (1955).

112. Chalkley, D. E. VAPOUR-PHASE CHROMATOGRAPHIC
ANALYSIS OF HYDROCARBON MIXTURES. Presented
at a Symposium in Stevenson, Scotland, May, 1955;
Abstract in Anal. Chem., 27, 1667 (1955).

113. Clough, K. H. ANALYSIS OF GASEOUS MIXTURES WITH
A NEW UNIT. Petrol. Engr. 27 (10), C 26-31 (1955);
C. A. 49, 14574 (1955).

114.   Dijkstra, G. , Keppler, J. G. and Schols, J. A.   GAS-
       LIQUID PARTITION CHROMATOGRAPHY, Rec. trav.
       chim. 74, 805-12 (1955); C. A. 50, 1528e (1956).

115.   Evans, D. E. M. and Tatlow, J. C.   THE GAS-CHROMA-
       TOGRAPHIC SEPARATION ON A PREPARATIVE SCALE,
       AND SOME REACTIONS OF 3H- AND 4H- NONAFLUORO-
       CYCLOHEXENE, J. Chem. Soc. 1955, 1184-88; C. A. 50,
       1617a (1956).

116.   Giddings, J. C. and Eyring, H.   A MOLECULAR DYNAMIC
       THEORY OF CHROMATOGRAPHY.   J. Phys. Chem. 59,
       416-21 (1955).

117.   Glueckauf, E.   THE THEORETICAL PLATE CONCEPT
       IN COLUMN SEPARATIONS, Trans. Faraday Soc. 51,
       34-44 (1955).

118.   Glueckauf, E.   THEORY OF CHROMATOGRAPHY. X.
       FORMULAE FOR DIFFUSION INTO SPHERES AND THEIR
       APPLICATION TO CHROMATOGRAPHY.   Trans. Faraday
       Soc.   51, 1540-51 (1955).

119.   Hagdahl, L.   COUPLED COLUMNS IN CHROMATOG-
       RAPHY.   Sci. Tools 1, 21-28 (1955).

120.   Hardy, C. J.   THESIS, University of Bristol, England.
       (1955).

121.   Hardy, C. J.   GAS PHASE CHROMATOGRAPHY AS AN
       ANALYTICAL TECHNIQUE, Presented at Western Sect. ,
       Soc. for Anal. Chem. , Cardiff, Wales; Anal. Chem. 27,
       470 (1955) abstract.

122.   Harvey, D. and Chalkley, D. E.   GAS-LIQUID CHROMA-
       TOGRAPHY, Fuel 34, 191-200 (1955); C. A. 49, 7436i (1955).

123.   Hoare, M. R. and Purnell, J. H.   TEMPERATURE
       EFFECTS IN GAS PHASE PARTITION CHROMATOG-
       RAPHY, Research Correspondence 8,   S41-S42 (1955);
       C. A. 49, 15362d (1955).

124.   I. E. C. Reports GAS-LIQUID CHROMATOGRAPHY,
       Ind. Eng. Chem. 47, (10), 13A, 14A, 16A, (1955)

166 BIBLIOGRAPHY 1955

125. James, A. T.   A NEW KIND OF CHROMATOGRAM.
Times Science Rev. 16, 8 (1955).

126. James, A. T. GAS-LIQUID CHROMATOGRAPHY, Chem.
Age (London)73, 733-36 (1955).

127. James, A. T. SEPARATION OF VOLATILE MATERIALS
BY GAS-LIQUID CHROMATOGRAPHY, Mfg. Chemist 26,
5-10 (1955); Chem. & Proc. Eng. 36, (3), 95-100 (1955).

128. James, A. T.   A NEW TECHNIQUE FOR THE SEPARA-
TION OF VOLATILE MATERIALS, Research (London) 8,
8-16 (1955); C. A. 49, 8028i (1955).

129. James, A. T.   and Martin, A. J. P. GAS-LIQUID CHRO-
MATOGRAPHY. A TECHNIQUE FOR THE ANALYSIS
AND IDENTIFICATION OF VOLATILE MATERIALS.
Chim. anal. 37, 321-26 (1955).

130. Janak, J. CHROMATOGRAPHY ANALYSIS AND SEPARA-
TION OF GASES. Paliva 35, 357-416 (1955); C. A. 50,
8173 (1956).

131. Janak, J. and Rusek, M. CHROMATOGRAPHIC SEMI-
MICROANALYSIS OF GASES. XI. DIRECT DETERMINA-
TION OF INDIVIDUAL OLEFINS IN GASES, Chem. listy
49, 191-99 (1955); C. A. 49, 8047g (1955); Collection
Czechoslov. Chem. Communs. 20, 923-32 (1955).

132. Janak, J. , Rusek, M. and Lazarev, A. CHROMATOG-
RAPHIC SEMI-MICROANALYSIS OF GASES. XII. SEPA-
RATION AND ANALYSIS OF GASEOUS CYCLOPARAFFINS,
Chem. listy 49, 700-05 (1955); C. A. 49, 12201h (1955).

133. Janak, J. USE OF ZEOLITES IN GAS CHROMATOGRAPHY.
PRELIMINARY COMMUNICATION, Chem. listy 49, 1403-
1405 (1955); C. A. 50, 104b (1956).

134. Kamer, J. H. van de, Gerritsma, K. W. and Wansink, E. J.
GAS-LIQUID PARTITION CHROMATOGRAPHY: THE
SEPARATION AND MICRO-ESTIMATION OF VOLATILE
FATTY ACIDS FROM FORMIC ACID TO DODECANOIC
ACID. Biochem. J. , 61, 174-76 (1955); C. A. 49, 15641
(1955).

135. Keppler, J. G. APPLICATION OF VAPOUR-PHASE
      CHROMATOGRAPHY. Chem. Weekblad 51, 911-14 (1955).

136. Keulemans, A. I. M., Kwantes, A. and Zaal, P. THE
      SELECTIVITY OF THE STATIONARY PHASE IN VAPOR
      PHASE CHROMATOGRAPHY. Anal. Chim. Acta 13,
      357-72 (1955).

137. Keulemans, A. I. M. and Kwantes, A. ANALYSIS OF
      VOLATILE ORGANIC COMPOUNDS BY VAPOUR-PHASE
      CHROMATOGRAPHY, 4th World Petrol Congr. , 1955;
      Fuel Abstr. 18, No. 3707 (1955).

138. Knox, J. H. APPLICATION OF GAS PHASE PARTITION
      CHROMATOGRAPHY TO COMPETITIVE CHLORINATION
      REACTIONS, Chem. & Ind. (London) 1955, 1631-32; C. A.
      50, 13713 (1956).

139. Kokes, R. J. , Tobin, H. , Jr. and Emmett, P. H.   A
      NEW MICROCATALYTIC-CHROMATOGRAPHIC TECH-
      NIQUE FOR STUDYING CATALYTIC REACTIONS, J. Am.
      Chem. Soc. 77, 5860-62 (1955).

140. Lederer, E. and Lederer, M. CHROMATOGRAPHY,
      Elsevier Pub. Co. , New York (1955).

141. Lichtenfels, D. H. , Fleck, S. A. and Burow, F. H. GAS-
      LIQUID PARTITION CHROMATOGRAPHY, Anal. Chem.
      27, 1510-13 (1955).

142. Littlewood, A. B. TECHNIQUES USED IN A STUDY OF
      THE BORON AND SILICON HYDRIDES, (abstracted) Anal.
      Chem. 27, 1667 (1955).

143. Littlewood, A. B. , Phillips, C. S. G. and Price, D. T.
      THE CHROMATOGRAPHY OF GASES AND VAPOURS.
      V. PARTITION ANALYSES WITH COLUMNS OF SILI-
      CONE 702 AND OF TRITOLYL PHOSPHATE, J. Chem.
      Soc. 1955, 1480-89; C. A. 49, 10800h (1955).

144. Martin, A. E. and Smart, J. GAS-PHASE CHROMATOG-
      RAPHY, Nature 175, 422-23, (1955); C. A. 49, 9334h (1955).

145. Martin, A. J. P. GAS-LIQUID CHROMATOGRAPHY.
      (abstracted) Anal. Chem. 27, 1667 (1955) with discussion

by R. F. G. Herrington, Analyst 81, 52-55 (1956).

146. Medvedeva, N. I. , and Torsueve, E. S. CHROMATOG-
      RAPHIC METHOD OF SEPARATING PRODUCTS FROM
      CRACKING OF HYDROCARBONS. Trudy Komissii Anal.
      Khim. Akad. Nauk. S. S. S. R. 6, 88-96 (1955); Fuel
      Abstr. No. 933 (1957).

147. Moore, W. R. VAPOR-PHASE CHROMATOGRAPHY,
      Presented at Joint Meet. of Organic and Medicinal Chem.
      Divisions of the Amer. Chem. Soc. , Minneapolis, Minn.,
      Sept. 1955.

148. Müller, R. H. PORTABLE APPARATUS ANALYZES
      MULTI-COMPONENT MIXTURES BY FRACTIONAL
      SEPARATION OF VAPORS IN PARTITION COLUMNS,
      Anal. Chem. 27, (6), 33A-36A (1955).

149. Nebbia, L. and Pagani, B. CHROMATOGRAPHIC DETER-
      MINATION OF ACETYLENE AND DIACETYLENE IN THE
      PRESENCE OF MONOSUBSTITUTED ACETYLENES,
      Chim. et ind. 37, (3) 200-01 (1955); Anal. Abstracts 2,
      No. 2114, (1955).

150. Patton, H. W. and Lewis, J. S. FRACTIONATION AND
      ANALYSIS ON A MICRO SCALE BY GAS CHROMATOG-
      RAPHY, Paper presented at 3rd. Natl. Air Poll. Symp.,
      Los Angeles, Calif. , Apr. 1955.

151. Patton, H. W. , Lewis, J. S. and Kaye, W. I. , THE SEPA-
      RATION AND ANALYSIS OF GASES AND VOLATILE
      LIQUIDS BY GAS CHROMATOGRAPHY, Anal. Chem. 27,
      170-74 (1955).

152. Phillips, C. S. G. ADSORPTION AND PARTITION METH-
      ODS, (abstracted) Anal. Chem. 27, 1667 (1955).

153. Podbielniak, W. J. and Preston, S. T. NEW TOOL-VAPOR
      PHASE CHROMATOGRAPHY. Petrol. Refiner 34 (11),
      165-69 (1955); C. A. 50, 559 (1956).

154. Pollard, F. H. and Hardy, C. J. THE EFFECT OF TEM-
      PERATURE OF INJECTION UPON THE SEPARATION OF
      LIQUID MIXTURES BY GAS-PHASE CHROMATOGRAPHY,
      Chem. & Ind. (London) 1955, 1145-46.

155.   Porath, J.   CHARCOAL CHROMATOGRAPHY WITH A STEP-GRADED ADSORPTION COLUMN, Arkiv. Kemi 7, 535-37 (1955); C. A. 49, 7437c (1955).

156.   Purnell, J. H. and Spencer, M. S.   USE OF SOLUBILIZING AGENTS IN GAS-PHASE PARTITION CHROMATOGRAPHY, Nature 175, 988-89 (1955); C. A. 49, 12175h (1955).

157.   Ray, N. H.   A RAPID CHROMATOGRAPHIC METHOD FOR THE DETERMINATION OF IMPURITIES IN ETHYLENE, Analyst 80, 853-60 (1955); C. A. 50, 4714c (1956).

158.   Scott, R. P. W.   A NEW DETECTOR FOR VAPOUR-PHASE PARTITION CHROMATOGRAPHY, Nature 176, 793 (1955).

159.   Thomas, B. W.   GAS CHROMATOGRAPHY MAY DEVELOP INTO USEFUL PROCESS ANALYZER, Ind. Eng. Chem. 47, (6), 85A-88A (1955).

160.   Vioque, E.   COLUMN PARTITION CHROMATOGRAPHY AND ITS APPLICATION TO THE SEPARATION OF FATTY ACIDS, Grasas y aceites 6, 88-93 (1955); C. A. 50, 2191a (1956).

161.   Wilson, N. H.   VAPOUR PHASE CHROMATOGRAPHY, Chem. & Ind. (London), 1955, 225.

1956

162.   Adlard, E. R.   AN EVALUATION OF SOME POLYGLYCOLS USED AS STATIONARY PHASES FOR GAS-LIQUID PARTITION CHROMATOGRAPHY, See ref. 365.

163.   Ambrose, D. and Collerson, R. R.   USE OF GAS-LIQUID PARTITION CHROMATOGRAPHY AS A PREPARATIVE METHOD, Nature 177, 84 (1956); C. A. 50, 8262g (1956).

164.   Anderson, J. R.   PARTITION COEFFICIENTS FROM GAS-LIQUID PARTITION CHROMATOGRAPHY, J. Am. Chem. Soc. 78 , 5692-93 (1956).

165.   Anderson, J. R. and Napier, K. H.   VAPOUR PHASE CHROMATOGRAPHIC SEPARATION OF AROMATICS FROM SATURATED·AND OLEFINIC HYDROCARBONS, Australian J. Chem. 9, 541-43 (1956).

166. Andronikashvili, T. G. and Kuz'mina, L. P. CHROMA-
TOGRAPHIC ANALYSIS OF SATURATED HYDROCARBONS
C_3 - C_7 ON NATURAL SORBENTS, Zavodskaya Lab. 22,
1403 (1956).

167. Bellis, H. E. and Slowinski, E. J. , Jr. APPLICATION OF
VAPOR CHROMATOGRAPHY TO INFRARED SPECTROS-
COPY OF LIQUIDS, J. Chem. Phys. 25, 794 (1956).

168. Benedek, P. and Szepesy, L. OBTAINING PURE ACETY-
LENE CONTENT BY CONTINUOUS GAS CHROMATOG-
RAPHY. Erdöl u. Kohle 9, 593-97 (1956).

169. Blom, L. and Edelhausen, L. VAPOUR PHASE CHRO-
MATOGRAPHIC DETERMINATION OF BENZENE, NAPH-
THALENE AND OTHER HYDROCARBONS IN WASH OIL.
Anal. Chim. Acta 15, 559-66 (1956).

170. Boer, H. A COMPARISON OF DETECTION METHODS
FOR GAS CHROMATOGRAPHY INCLUDING DETECTION
BY BETA RAY IONIZATION, See ref. 365.

171. Bosanquet, C. H. and Morgan, G. O. THE CONCENTRA-
TION FACTOR IN VAPOUR PHASE CHROMATOGRAPHY.
See ref. 365.

172. Brennan, D. and Kemball, C. GAS PHASE CHROMATOG-
RAPHY, A CLASS EXPERIMENT, J. Chem. Educ. 33,
490-92 (1956).

173. Brenner, N. APPLICATIONS OF GAS CHROMATOGRAPHY
TO TIOLET-GOODS ANALYSIS. Proc. Sci. Sect. Toilet
Goods Assoc. 26, 3-8 (1956); C. A. 51, 3934 (1957).

174. Brooks, J. , Murray, W. and Williams, A. F. APPARA-
TUS FOR VAPOUR PHASE CHROMATOGRAPHY WITH
AUXILIARY UNIT FOR THE DETERMINATION OF ISO-
PROPYL NITRATE IN HEAVY OILS, See ref. 365.

175. Brooks, V. T. and Collins, G. A. GAS-LIQUID CHROMA-
TOGRAPHY. SEPARATION USING VARIOUS STATIONARY
PHASES, Chem. & Ind. (London) 1956, 921; C. A. 51, 3234h
(1957).

176. Brooks, V. T. and Collins, G. A. SEPARATION OF

PYRIDINE BASES BY VAPOUR PHASE CHROMATOG-
RAPHY, Chem. & Ind. (London) 1956, 1021; C.A. 51,
2355 (1957).

177.   Bucur, R.   CHROMOTHERMOGRAPHIC ANALYSIS OF
       GASEOUS HYDROCARBONS, Rev. Chim. (Bucharest) 7,
       163 (1956).

178.   Buzon, J. and Moghadame, P.E.   VAPOR-PHASE PARTI-
       TION CHROMATOGRAPHY, Rev. inst. franc. petrole 11,
       1616-28 (1956).

179.   Caroti, G.   CHROMATOGRAPHY OF GAS-TECHNIQUE
       OF GAS LIQUID DISTRIBUTION. Riv. combustibli 10,
       456-71 (1956);   C.A. 50, 15324 (1956).

180.   Cecil, O.B. and Munch, R.H.   THERMAL CONDUCTIVITY
       OF SOME ORGANIC LIQUIDS, Ind. Eng. Chem. 48, 437-40
       (1956).

181.   Chemodanova, L. S. and Turkeltaub, N.M.   CHROMATO-
       THERMOGRAPHIC METHOD OF DETERMINING BENZENE,
       TOLUENE, ISOPENTANE, HEXANE, AND ISO-OCTANE,
       Zavodskaya Lab. 22, 1406-07 (1956).

182.   Clough, K.H.   OPERATING YOUR GAS CHROMATOG-
       RAPHIC UNIT.   Presented at 21st Meeting of Gulf Coast
       Spectroscopic Group, Baton Rouge, Louisiana, September
       1956.   Abstract in Anal. Chem. 29, 166 (1957).

183.   Coates, V.J. and Brenner, N.   FUEL GAS ANALYSIS BY
       CHROMATOGRAPHY, Petrol. Refiner 35, (11), 197-201
       (1956);   C.A. 51, 1587 (1957).

184.   Colburn, C.B.   THE USE OF VAPOR PHASE CHROMA-
       TOGRAPHY IN KINETIC INVESTIGATIONS. I.   THE
       THERMAL DECOMPOSITION OF NEOPENTYL NITRATE,
       Presented at Symp. on Vapor-Phase Chromatography,
       129th Natl. ACS meeting, Dallas, Texas, April 1956.

185.   Coppens, L., Venter, J. and Bricteux, J.   NOTES ON
       GAS CHROMATOGRAPHY, Inst. Nat. ind. Charbonniere,
       Bull. tech.   Houille et derives 1956, 311-44; C.A. 51,
       5386g (1957).

186. Corbin, J.R. and Coates, V.J. THE QUALITATIVE AND QUANTITATIVE ANALYSIS OF MULTICOMPONENT MIX-TURES BY VAPOR FRACTOMETRY, Presented at Pitts-burgh Conference on Anal. Chem. & Appl. Spect., February 1956.

187. Cordon, J.L.M. and Lopez, G.Z. SEPARATION OF VOLATILE ORGANIC COMPOUNDS BY VAPOR-PHASE CHROMATOGRAPHY. Combustibiles (Zaragoza) 16, 65-75 (1956); J. Inst. Petrol. Abstr. No. 1566 (1956).

188. Cornforth, J.W. and James, A.T. STRUCTURE OF A NATURALLY OCCURRING ANTAGONIST OF DIHYDRO-STREPTOMYCIN (Use of Gas Chromatography). Biochem. J. 63, 124-30 (1956).

189. Craats, F. van de. APPLICATIONS OF VAPOUR-PHASE CHROMATOGRAPHY IN THE GAS-ANALYTICAL FIELD. Anal. Chim. Acta 14, 136-39 (1956).

190. Cropper, F.R. and Heywood, A. THE ANALYSIS OF FATTY ACIDS AND FATTY ALCOHOLS BY VAPOUR-PHASE CHROMATOGRAPHY. See ref. 365.

191. Cvetanovic, R.J. and Kutschke, K.O. MICRO-VAPOUR PHASE CHROMATOGRAPHY - EFFECT OF COLUMN TEMPERATURE. See ref. 365.

192. Davies, A.J. and Johnson, J.K. A THERMAL CONDUC-TIVITY DETECTOR FOR USE AT HIGH TEMPERATURES IN VAPOUR PHASE CHROMATOGRAPHY, See ref. 365.

193. Davis, A.D. and Howard, G.A. THE USE OF THERMIS-TOR DETECTORS IN GAS CHROMATOGRAPHY, Chem.& Ind. B.I.F. Review, April 1956, R25-R26; C.A. 50, 15135 (1956).

194. Dawson, H.J., Jr. and Schmauch, L.J. APPLICATIONS OF VAPOR-PHASE PARTITION CHROMATOGRAPHY TO THE ANALYSIS OF CATALYTIC REFORMATES, Presented at Symp. on Vapor Phase Chromatography, 129th Natl. ACS meeting, Dallas, Texas, April 1956.

195. Deal, C.H., Otvos, J.W., Smith, V.N. and Zucco, P.S. A RADIOLOGICAL DETECTOR FOR GAS CHROMATOG-

RAPHY, Anal. Chem. <u>28</u>, 1958-64 (1956).

196. Desty, D. H. , Warham, T. J. and Whyman, B. H. F. THE
      APPLICATION OF VAPOUR PHASE CHROMATOGRAPHY
      TO THE EXAMINATION OF SAMPLES TAKEN FROM
      INTERNAL COMBUSTION ENGINES BY AN OPEN-HOLE
      TECHNIQUE, See ref. 365.

197. Dewhurst, H. A. RADIATION CHEMISTRY OF n-HEXANE
      AND CYCLOHEXANE LIQUIDS. (Use of Gas Chromatog-
      raphy). J. Chem. Phys. <u>24</u>, 1253-55 (1956).

198. Dimbat, M. , Porter, P. E. and Stross, F. H. APPARATUS
      REQUIREMENTS FOR QUANTITATIVE APPLICATION OF
      GAS-LIQUID PARTITION CHROMATOGRAPHY, Anal.
      Chem. <u>28</u>, 290-97 (1956).

199. Dimick, K. P. and Corse, J. GAS CHROMATOGRAPHY,
      A NEW METHOD FOR THE SEPARATION AND IDENTI-
      FICATION OF VOLATILE MATERIALS IN FOODS, Food
      Technol. <u>10</u>, 360-64 (1956); C. A. <u>50</u>, 15979c (1956).

200. Dimick, K. P. and Makower, B. B. VOLATILE FLAVOR
      OF STRAWBERRY ESSENCE. I. IDENTIFICATION OF
      THE CARBONYLS AND CERTAIN LOW-BOILING SUB-
      STANCES, Food Technol. <u>10</u>, 73-75 (1956); C. A. <u>50</u>,
      12341a (1956).

201. Dimick, K. P. , Stitt, F. and Corse, J.   VOLATILE
      FLAVOR OF STRAWBERRIES. II. APPLICATION OF
      GAS-LIQUID PARTITION CHROMATOGRAPHY. Presented
      at Symp. on Vapor-Phase Chromatography, 129th Natl.
      ACS meeting, Dallas, Texas, April 1956.

202. Doering, W. V. , Buttery, R. G. , Laughlin, R. G. and
      Chaudhuri, N. INDISCRIMINATE REACTION OF
      METHYLENE WITH THE CARBON-HYDROGEN BOND.
      J. Am. Chem. Soc. <u>78</u>, 3224 (1956).

203. Drew, C. M. and McNesby, J. R. SOME PROBLEMS
      ENCOUNTERED WITH THE APPLICATION OF VAPOUR
      PHASE CHROMATOGRAPHY TO KINETIC STUDIES. See
      ref. 365.

204. Drew, C. M. and McNesby, J. R. THE APPLICATION OF
      VAPOR-PHASE CHROMATOGRAPHY TO THE STUDY OF

GAS PHASE REACTIONS, Presented at Symp. on Vapor
Phase Chromatography, 129th Natl. ACS meeting, Dallas,
Texas, April 1956.

205.   Drew, C. M. , McNesby, J. R. , Gordon, A. S. and Smith,
        S. R.   RECOVERY OF VAPOR-PHASE CHROMATOGRAPHY
        FRACTIONS AND THEIR ANALYSIS BY MASS SPECTRO-
        METRY, Presented at 4th Ann. Meet. ASTM Committee
        E-14 on Mass Spectro. , Cincinnati, Ohio, May 1956.

206.   Drew, C. M. , McNesby, J. R. , Smith, S. R. and Gordon,
        A. S.   APPLICATION OF VAPOR-PHASE CHROMATOG-
        RAPHY TO MASS SPECTROMETRIC ANALYSIS, Anal.
        Chem. 28, 979-83 (1956).

207.   Dudenbostel, B. F. , Jr. and Priestley, W. , Jr.   GAS
        CHROMATOGRAPHY FOR PROCESS CONTROL, Ind.
        Eng. Chem. 48, (9) 55A-56A, (1956).

208.   Ebeid, F. M. and Minkoff, G. J.   SENSITIVITY OF VAPOR-
        PHASE CHROMATOGRAPHY DETECTORS, Research
        Correspondence 9, S24 (1956).

209.   Eggertsen, P. T. , Knight, H. S. and Groennings, S.   USE
        OF LIQUID-MODIFIED SOLID ADSORBENT TO RESOLVE
        C_5 AND C_6 SATURATES, Anal. Chem. 28, 303-06 (1956).

210.   Evans, D. E. M. and Tatlow, J. C.   THE APPLICATION
        OF GAS CHROMATOGRAPHY TO ORGANIC FLUORINE
        CHEMISTRY, See ref. 365.

211.   Evans, J. B. and Willard, J. E.   USE OF GAS-PHASE
        CHROMATOGRAPHY FOR THE SEPARATION OF MIX-
        TURES OF CARRIER-FREE RADIOACTIVE SUBSTANCES:
        PRODUCTS OF CHEMICAL REACTIONS ACTIVATED BY
        NUCLEAR PROCESSES. J. Am. Chem. Soc. 78, 2908-09
        (1956).

212.   Ferrer, P.   GAS CHROMATOGRAPHY: NEW INSTRU-
        MENTS AND TECHNIQUE, Afinidad 33, 199-208 (1956).

213.   Fredericks, E. M. and Brooks, F. R.   ANALYSES OF
        GASEOUS HYDROCARBONS BY GAS-LIQUID CHROMA-
        TOGRAPHY, Anal. Chem. 28, 297-303 (1956).

214. Freund, M. , Benedek, P. and Szepesy, L. CHEMICAL
      ENGINEERING DESIGN OF A UNIT FOR CONTINUOUS
      GAS CHROMATOGRAPHY (HYPERSORPTION). See
      ref. 365.

215. Fuks, N. A. GAS LIQUID CHROMATOGRAPHY. Uspekhi,
      Khim. 25, 845-58 (1956); C. A. 50, 15324 (1956).

216. Fuller, D. H. GAS CHROMATOGRAPHY IN PLANT
      STREAMS. Instrument Soc. Am. J. 3, 440-44 (1956).

217. Glogoczowski, J. NEW TRENDS IN ANALYSIS OF GASEOUS
      HYDROCARBONS. Nafta (Poland) 12, 268-73 (1956); C. A.
      51, 16206 (1957).

218. Glueckauf, E. and Kitt, G. P. GAS CHROMATOGRAPHIC
      SEPARATION OF HYDROGEN ISOTOPES, See ref. 365.

219. Godsell, J. A. , Stacey, M. and Tatlow, J. C. HEXAFLU-
      OROBENZENE (USE OF PREPARATIVE SCALE GAS
      CHROMATOGRAPHY), Nature 178, 199-200 (1956).

220. Gohlke, R. S. and McLafferty, F. W. THE USE OF VAPOR
      PHASE CHROMATOGRAPHY IN THE IDENTIFICATION OF
      UNKNOWN MIXTURES, Presented at Symp. on Vapor -
      Phase Chromatography, 129th Natl. ACS meeting, Dallas,
      Texas, April 1956.

221. Grant, D. W. and Vaughan, G. A. A CONSIDERATION OF
      FACTORS GOVERNING THE SEPARATION OF SUBSTANCES
      BY GAS-LIQUID PARTITION CHROMATOGRAPHY, J.
      Appl. Chem. 6, 145-53 (1956).

222. Grant, D. W. and Vaughan, G. A. THE USE OF GAS-
      LIQUID CHROMATOGRAPHY IN THE DETERMINATION
      OF AROMATIC COMPOUNDS IN COAL TAR NAPHTHAS,
      See ref. 365.

223. Green, S. W. VAPOUR PHASE CHROMATOGRAPHY,
      Ind. Chemist 32, 24-28 (1956).

224. Green, S. W. THE QUANTITATIVE ANALYSIS OF MIX-
      TURES OF CHLOROFLUOROMETHANES, See ref. 365.

225. Greene, S. A. , Moberg, M. L. and Wilson, E. N.

SEPARATION OF GASES BY GAS ADSORPTION CHRO-
MATOGRAPHY, Anal. Chem. 28, 1369-70 (1956).

226. Grune, W. N. , Carter, J. Y. , Jr. and Keenan, J. P.
DEVELOPMENT OF A CONTINUOUS GAS CHROMATO-
GRAPHIC ANALYZER FOR SLUDGE DIGESTION STUDIES.
Sewage and Ind. Wastes 28 (12), 1433-42 (1956); C. A. 51,
3067 (1957).

227. Guild, L. V. SOME PRACTICAL APPLICATIONS OF GAS
CHROMATOGRAPHY, Presented at Pittsburgh Conference
on Anal. Chem. & Appl. Spec. , February 1956.

228. Guild, L. V. SOME APPLICATIONS OF THE ELUTION
AND DISPLACEMENT TECHNIQUE IN GAS-VAPOR
CHROMATOGRAPHY, Presented at Symp. on Vapor-Phase
Chromatography, 129th Natl. ACS Meeting, Dallas, Texas,
April 1956.

229. Harley, J. and Pretorius, V. NEW DETECTOR FOR
VAPOUR-PHASE CHROMATOGRAPHY. Nature 178,
1244 (1956).

230. Harrison, G. F. VAPOUR PHASE CHROMATOGRAPHIC
ANALYSIS OF CHLORINATED HYDROCARBONS AND
HYDROCARBON GASES, See ref. 365.

231. Harvey, D. and Morgan, G. O. FACTORS AFFECTING
THERMAL CONDUCTIVITY DETECTORS IN VAPOUR
PHASE PARTITION CHROMATOGRAPHY, See ref. 365.

232. Hausdorff, H. H. VAPOUR FRACTOMETRY (GAS CHRO-
MATOGRAPHY) PART II. A POWERFUL NEW TOOL IN
CHEMICAL ANALYSIS, See ref. 365.

233. Hawkes, J. C. THE CONSTRUCTION OF AN APPARATUS
FOR STUDIES IN VAPOUR PHASE CHROMATOGRAPHY
AT TEMPERATURES UP TO 300° C, See ref. 365.

234. Henderson, J. I. and Knox, J. H. THE MICRO-FLAME
DETECTOR IN GAS-LIQUID PARTITION CHROMATOG-
RAPHY: CORRELATION OF RESPONSE WITH HEATS OF
COMBUSTION, J. Chem. Soc. 1956, 2299-2302.

235. Herington, E. F. G. THE THERMODYNAMICS OF GAS-

LIQUID CHROMATOGRAPHY, See ref. 365.

236. Hoare, M.R. and Purnell, J.H. TEMPERATURE EF-
FECTS IN GAS-LIQUID PARTITION CHROMATOGRAPHY,
Trans. Faraday Soc. 52, 222-29 (1956).

237. Hrapia, H. and Könnecke, H.G. CHROMATOGRAPHIC
GAS ANALYSIS, J. prakt. Chem. 3, 106-12 (1956).

238. Hunter, I.R., Dimick, K.P. and Corse, J.W. DETER-
MINATION OF AMINO-ACIDS BY NINHYDRIN OXIDATION
AND GAS CHROMATOGRAPHY, Chem. & Ind. (London)
1956, 294-95.

239. James, A.T. GAS-LIQUID CHROMATOGRAPHY. SEPA-
RATION AND MICRO-ESTIMATION OF VOLATILE
AROMATIC AMINES, Anal. Chem. 28, 1564-67 (1956).

240. James, A.T. GAS-LIQUID CHROMATOGRAPHY, J.
Pharm. & Pharmacol. 8, 232-40 (1956); C.A. 50, 13370f
(1956).

241. James, A.T. GAS-LIQUID CHROMATOGRAPHY - A
METHOD OF SEPARATION AND IDENTIFICATION OF
VOLATILE MATERIALS, Can. Chem, Processing 1956,
111-14, a review.

242. James, A.T. DETECTION OF VAPORS IN FLOWING
GAS STREAMS, See ref. 365.

243. James, A.T. THE GAS-LIQUID CHROMATOGRAM,
Endeavour 15, 73-78 (1956); C.A. 51, 42 (1957).

244. James, A.T. and Martin, A.J.P. GAS-LIQUID CHRO-
MATOGRAPHY. THE SEPARATION AND IDENTIFICA-
TION OF THE METHYL ESTERS OF SATURATED AND
UNSATURATED ACIDS FROM FORMIC TO n-OCTADE-
CANOIC ACID, Biochem. J. 63, 144-52 (1956).

245. James, A.T. and Martin, A.J.P. SEPARATION AND
IDENTIFICATION OF SOME VOLATILE PARAFFINIC,
NAPHTHENIC, OLEFINIC, AND AROMATIC HYDRO-
CARBONS, J. Appl. Chem. 6, 105-15 (1956).

246. James, A.T., Peeters, G. and Lauryssens, M. THE

METABOLISM OF PROPIONIC ACID. Biochem. J. 64, 726-30 (1956).

247. James, A. T. and Wheatley, V. R. DETERMINATION OF THE COMPONENT FATTY ACIDS OF HUMAN FOREARM SEBUM BY GAS-LIQUID CHROMATOGRAPHY, Biochem. J. 63, 269-73, (1956); C. A. 50, 14907g (1956).

248. Janak, J. SYSTEMATIC CHROMATOGRAPHIC MICRO-ANALYSIS OF GASES, Mikrochim. Acta 1956, 1038-49; C. A. 50, 10377e (1956).

249. Janak, J. NEW METHODS OF GAS ANALYSIS. GAS CHROMATOGRAPHY, Chem. Tech. (Berlin) 8, 125-32 (1956); Fuel Abstr. 20, No. 3427, (1956).

250. Janak, J. CHROMATOGRAPHIC ANALYSIS OF CONNATE WATER IN OIL PROSPECTING, Prace Ustavu pro naftovy vyzkum. Ser. E. No. 17/21, 5-24 (Russian and German Summary 25-28) (1956); C. A. 50, 16083d (1956).

251. Janak, J. THE CONCEPT OF THE CHROMATOGRAPHIC SPECTRUM OF GASES AND VOLATILE MATERIALS, See ref. 365.

252. Janak, J. VAPOUR PHASE CHROMATOGRAPHY ON ZEOLITES, See ref. 365.

253. Johnson, H. W. , Jr. LIQUID SUBSTRATES AND THE GAS-LIQUID PARTITION COLUMN, Presented at Symp. on Vapor-Phase Chromatography, 129th Natl. ACS meeting, Dallas, Texas, April 1956.

254. Kearns, R. and Guild, L. V. AN APPARATUS FOR ANALYSIS BY GAS CHROMATOGRAPHY METHOD, Presented at the Pittsburgh Conference on Anal. Chem. & Appl. Spec. , February 1956.

255. Keppler, J. G. , Dijkstra, G. and Schols, J. A. VAPOUR PHASE CHROMATOGRAPHY AT HIGH TEMPERATURES, See ref. 365.

256. Keppler, J. G. , Schols, J. A. and Dijkstra, G.   A MULTIPLE GAS CHROMATOGRAPHIC APPARATUS FOR USE AT TEMPERATURES UP TO 250°C, Rec. trav.

chim. 75, 965-76 (1956); C. A. 50, 15135 (1956).

257.   Keulemans, A. I. M. and Kwantes, A. FACTORS DETER-
       MINING COLUMN EFFICIENCY IN GAS-LIQUID PARTI-
       TION CHROMATOGRAPHY, See ref. 365.

258.   Klinkenberg, A. and Sjinitzer, F. HOLDING-TIME DIS-
       TRIBUTIONS OF THE GAUSSIAN TYPE. Chem. Eng.
       Sci. 5, 258-70 (1956).

259.   Kovats, E. and Heilbronner, E. STANDARD-SUBSTANCE
       METHOD IN GAS CHROMATOGRAPHIC CHARACTERIZA-
       TION OF ORGANIC COMPOUNDS, Chimia (Switz.) 10,
       288-89 (1956).

260.   Krivoruchko, F. D. and Turkeltaub, N. M. CHROMATO-
       GRAPHIC METHOD OF SEPARATE DETERMINATION OF
       DIVINYL, ETHYLBENZENE, AND STYRENE IN AIR,
       Zavodskaya Lab. 22, 1408 (1956).

261.   Lemmon, R. M. , Mazetti, F. , Reynolds, F. L. and Calvin,
       M. LABELING OF BENZENE WITH A CARBON-14 ION
       BEAM. (SEPARATION OF PRODUCTS BY GAS-LIQUID
       CHROMATOGRAPHY), J. Am. Chem. Soc. 78, 6414-15
       (1956).

262.   Levy, E. J. , Lawrey, D. M. G. , Herk, L. P. , Jr. and
       Stahl, W. H. THE APPLICATION OF ISOLATIVE VAPOR
       PHASE CHROMATOGRAPHY AND MASS SPECTROMETRY
       TO PROBLEMS IN ODOR RESEARCH, Presented at 4th
       Ann. Meet. ASTM Committee E-14 on Mass Spectrometry,
       Cincinnati, Ohio, May 1956.

263.   Lewis, J. S. , Patton, H. W. and Kaye, W. I. QUALITATIVE
       GAS CHROMATOGRAPHIC ANALYSIS USING TWO COL -
       UMNS OF DIFFERENT CHARACTERISTICS, Anal. Chem.
       28, 1370-73 (1956).

264.   Liberti, A. , Cartoni, G. and Pallotta, V. COULOMETRIC
       MICRODETERMINATION OF VOLATILE FAT ACIDS IN
       DAIRY PRODUCTS AS SEPARATED BY VAPOR-PHASE
       CHROMATOGRAPHY, Latte 30, 581-84 (1956).

265.   Liberti, A. , Conti, L. and Crescenzi, V. MOLECULAR
       WEIGHT DETERMINATION OF COMPONENTS BY GAS-

PHASE CHROMATOGRAPHY, Nature 178, 1067-69 (1956);
C. A. 51, 8508e (1957).

266. Lichtenfels, D. H. , Fleck, S. A. , Burow, F. H. and Cog-
      geshall, N. D.   GAS PARTITION ANALYSIS OF LIGHT
      ENDS IN GASOLINE, Anal. Chem. 28, 1376-79 (1956).

267. Lotz, J. R. and Willingham, C. B.   GAS-PHASE CHROMA-
      TOGRAPHY, J. Chem. Educ. 33, 485-89 (1956) - survey.

268. Lotz, J. R. and Willingham, C. B.   GAS CHROMATOG-
      RAPHY: A MEANS FOR SEPARATION AND ANALYSIS OF
      VOLATILE MATERIALS. Ind. Hyg. Foundation Am. Trans.
      Bull. No. 30, 195-200 (1956); C. A. 51, 11157 (1957).

269. Martin, A. J. P.   GAS-LIQUID CHROMATOGRAPHY.
      Experientia, Suppl. No. 5, 21-32 (1956); C. A. 51, 7221
      (1957).

270. Martin, A. J. P.   TRENDS IN GAS CHROMATOGRAPHY,
      See ref. 365.

271. Martin, A. J. P., Chalkley, D. E. , Littlewood, A. B. ,
      Phillips, C. S. G. , Ray, N. H. , Keulemans, A. I. M. ,
      Herington, E. F. G.   SYMPOSIUM ON GAS CHROMATOG-
      RAPHY, Analyst 81, 52-58 (1956).

272. Martin, A. J. P. and James, A. T.   GAS-LIQUID CHROMA-
      TOGRAPHY. THE GAS-DENSITY METER, A NEW APPA-
      RATUS FOR THE DETECTION OF VAPORS IN FLOWING
      GAS STREAM, Biochem. J. 63, 138-43 (1956); C. A. 50,
      1366g (1956).

273. Martinez, C. J. L. and Zazurca, L. G.   SEPARATION OF
      ORGANIC VOLATILE COMPOUNDS BY VAPOR PHASE
      CHROMATOGRAPHY, Combustibles 16, 65-75 (1956);
      Fuel Abstr. 20, No. 3425 (1956).

274. McInnes, A. G.   PRACTICAL NOTES ON GAS-LIQUID
      CHROMATOGRAPHY AS APPLIED TO THE ESTIMATION
      OF VOLATILE FATTY ACIDS, See ref. 365.

275. McNesby, J. R. , Drew, C. M. and Gordon, A. S.   MECHA-
      NISM OF THE DECOMPOSITION OF PRIMARY AND
      SECONDARY n-BUTYL FREE RADICALS, J. Chem. Phys.

<u>24</u>, 1260 (1956).

276. Mellor, N. FACTORS AFFECTING KATHAROMETER
SENSITIVITY AND COLUMN EFFICIENCY IN VAPOUR
PHASE PARTITION CHROMATOGRAPHY, See ref. 365.

277. Miller, C. T. GAS CHROMATOGRAPHY, Research and
Eng. <u>2</u> (2), 26-27 (1956).

278. Munday, C. W. and Primavesi, G. R. PROPERTIES OF
THE MARTIN GAS DENSITY BALANCE AND POSSIBLE
MODIFICATIONS THEREOF, See ref. 365.

279. Murray, W. J. and Williams, A. F. THE DETERMINA-
TION OF SMALL AMOUNTS OF PICOLINE IN AQUEOUS
SOLUTIONS OF PICOLINE BY VAPOUR PHASE CHROMA-
TOGRAPHY, Chem. & Ind. (London) <u>1956</u>, 1020-21; C. A.
<u>51</u>, 2473 (1957).

280. Niegisch, W. D. and Stahl, W. H. THE ONION: GASEOUS
EMANATION PRODUCTS. Food Research <u>21</u>, 657-65 (1956).

281. Otvos, J. W. and Stevenson, D. P. CROSS-SECTIONS OF
MOLECULES FOR IONIZATION BY ELECTRONS. J. Am.
Chem. Soc. <u>78</u>, 546-51 (1956).

282. Patton, H. W. USE OF ADSORBENTS IN VAPOR-PHASE
CHROMATOGRAPHY, Presented at Symp. on Vapor-Phase
Chromatography, 129th Natl. ACS meeting, Dallas, Texas,
April 1956.

283. Patton, H. W. and Touey, G. P. GAS CHROMATOGRAPHIC
DETERMINATION OF SOME HYDROCARBONS IN CIGA-
RETTE SMOKE, Anal. Chem. <u>28,</u> 1685-88 (1956).

284. Percival, W. C. QUANTITATIVE ANALYSIS OF 'FREON'
FLUORINATED HYDROCARBONS BY VAPOR-PHASE
CHROMATOGRAPHY, Paper presented at Pittsburgh
Conference on Anal. Chem. & Appl. Spec., February 1956.

285. Peyrot, P. VAPOR PHASE PARTITION CHROMATOG-
RAPHY. Rev. franc. corps. gras. <u>3</u> (7), 552 (1956).

286. Phillips, C. S. G. GAS CHROMATOGRAPHY, Academic
Press, Inc., New York, 1956.

287.   Pierotti, G. J., Deal, C. H., Derr, E. L. and Porter, P. E.
       SOLVENT EFFECTS IN GAS-LIQUID PARTITION CHRO-
       MATOGRAPHY, J. Am. Chem. Soc. 78, 2989-98 (1956).

288.   Podbielniak, W. J. and Preston, S. T.   VAPOR-PHASE
       CHROMATOGRAPHY, Petrol. Refiner 35, (4), 215-20
       (1956); C. A. 50, 8368f (1956).

289.   Podbielniak, W. J. and Preston, S. T.   VAPOR-PHASE
       CHROMATOGRAPHIC EQUIPMENT, Oil Gas J. 54, (50),
       211-12, 215-16, 219 (1956); C. A. 51, 4773e (1957).

290.   Pollard, F. H. and Hardy, C. J. THE APPLICATION OF
       VAPOUR PHASE CHROMATOGRAPHY TO THE PREPA-
       RATION OF PURE MATERIALS, Chem. & Ind. (London)
       1956, 527-28.

291.   Pollard, F. H. and Hardy, C. J. A PRELIMINARY STUDY
       OF SOME FACTORS INFLUENCING THE ORDER OF
       ELUTION OF HALOGENATED METHANES, THE DEGREE
       OF SEPARATION, AND THE REPRODUCIBILITY OF
       RETENTION VOLUMES IN GAS-LIQUID PARTITION
       CHROMATOGRAPHY, See ref. 365.

292.   Porter, P. E., Deal, C. H. and Stross, F. H. THE DETER-
       MINATION OF PARTITION COEFFICIENTS FROM GAS-
       LIQUID PARTITION CHROMATOGRAPHY. J. Am. Chem.
       Soc. 78, 2999-3006 (1956).

293.   Pretorius, V. GAS CHROMATOGRAPHY, S. African Ind.
       Chemist 10, 303-08 (1956); C. A. 51, 5501 (1957).

294.   Price, A. R. ANALYSIS OF LIGHT HYDROCARBON MIX-
       TURES BY GAS CHROMATOGRAPHY, Presented at 3rd
       Ann. Technological Meet. of Sabine Area Sec. A. I. Ch. E.
       and Texas-Louisiana Gulf Sec. ACS, Beaumont, Texas,
       March 1956.

295.   Purnell, J. H. A BASIS FOR THE COMPARISON AND
       CHOICE OF SOLVENTS IN VAPOUR PHASE PARTITION
       CHROMATOGRAPHY, See ref. 365.

296.   Rangel, T. THESIS, Rice Institute, 1956.

297.   Robb, J. C. and Vofsi, D. THE QUANTITATIVE SEPA-

RATION OF MIXTURES CONTAINING VINYL ACETATE
AND BROMOTRICHLOROMETHANE BY VAPOUR PHASE
CHROMATOGRAPHY, See ref. 365.

298. Rock, H. GAS CHROMATOGRAPHY AND EXTRACTIVE
DISTILLATION, Chem. -Ing. Tech. 28, 489-95 (1956);
C. A. 50, 14311e (1956).

299. Rouit, C. CHROMATOGRAPHIC ANALYSIS OF GASES
AND VAPOURS, Rev. Inst. franc. petrole 11, 213-30 (1956);
J. Inst. Petrol. Abstr. No. 1368, (1956); C. A. 50, 13660
(1956).

300. Rouit, C. THE ANALYSIS AND CONTROL OF REFINERY
GAS STREAMS USING THE CHROMATOGRAPHIC TECH-
NIQUE (JANAK METHOD), See ref. 365.

301. Scott, R. P. W. A NEW DETECTOR FOR VAPOUR PHASE
PARTITION CHROMATOGRAPHY, See ref. 365.

302. Seligman, R. B. , Resnik, F. E. , O'Keefe, A. E. , Holmes,
J. C. , Morrell, F. A. , Murrill, D. P. and Gager, F. L. , Jr.
VAPOR-PHASE CHROMATOGRAPHY IN TOBACCO RE-
SEARCH, Presented at Symp. on Vapor-Phase Chromatog-
raphy, 129th Natl. ACS meeting, Dallas, Texas, April 1956.

303. Simon, R. H. M. GAS CHROMATOGRAPHY. Chem. Eng.
News 34, 2350 (1956).

304. Sloman, K. G. and Borker, E. VAPOR PHASE CHROMA-
TOGRAPHY - A PRELIMINARY INVESTIGATION OF
APPLICATIONS IN A FOOD LABORATORY, Presented
at Symp. on Vapor-Phase Chromatography, 129th Natl.
ACS Meeting, Dallas, Texas, April 1956.

305. Sorensen, I. and Soltoft, P. LOW RESISTANCE VAPOUR-
PHASE CHROMATOGRAPH COLUMN, Acta Chem. Scand.
10, 1673-74 (1956).

306. Straten, H. A. van. CHROMATOGRAPHIC GAS ANALYSIS.
Zakenwerald (Amsterdam) 34, 46 (1956).

307. Sullivan, L. J. , Lotz, J. R. and Willingham, C. B. RETEN-
TION VOLUMES OF ISOMERIC HEXENES AND HEXANES
IN GAS-LIQUID PARTITION CHROMATOGRAPHY USING

PHTHALATE ESTERS AS LIQUID PHASE, Anal. Chem. 28, 495-98 (1956).

308. Sunner, S. , Karrman, K. J. and Sunden, V. SEPARATION OF MERCAPTANS BY GAS-LIQUID PARTITION CHROMA-TOGRAPHY, Mikrochim. Acta 1956, 1144-51 (in English); C. A. 50, 8396e (1956).

309. Sventsitskiy, E. I. , Lulova, N. I. , Tarasov, A. I. and Semskova, E. I. ANALYSIS OF HYDROCARBON GASES BY THE CHROMATHERMOGRAPHIC METHOD, Zavod-skaya Lab. 22, 1399-1403 (1956).

310. Taramasso, M. VAPOR PHASE CHROMATOGRAPHY OF GASEOUS HYDROCARBONS. Ricerca sci. 26, 887-88 (1956); C. A. 50, 9944 (1956).

311. Taramasso, M. VAPOR PHASE CHROMATOGRAPHIC ANALYSIS OF SATURATED HYDROCARBON GASES. Termotecnica (Milan) 10, 203-06 (1956); C. A. 51, 2260 (1957).

312. Tarmy, B. L. THE APPLICATION OF FREQUENCY RESPONSE ANALYSIS TO THE MEASUREMENT OF THERMAL CONDUCTIVITY OF GASES,   THESIS Columbia University, 1956.

313. Taylor, B. W. DEVELOPMENT OF COMPONENTS OF AN INSTRUMENT FOR RESEARCH AND CONTROL APPLICATIONS OF VAPOR PHASE CHROMATOGRAPHY, Presented at Symp. on Vapor-Phase Chromatography, 129th Natl. ACS Meeting, Dallas, Texas, April 1956.

314. Turkeltaub, N. M. , Zolotareva, O. V. , Latukhova, A. G. , Karymova, A. I. and Kalnina, E. CHROMATOGRAPHIC METHOD FOR THE SEPARATION OF HYDROGEN, CAR-BON MONOXIDE, METHANE AND A MIXTURE OF RARE GASES, Zhur. Anal. Khim. 11, 159-66 (1956); C. A. 50, 14446g (1956).

315. Turkeltaub, N. M. , Porshneva, N. V. and Kancheeva, O. A. CHROMATOGRAPHIC THERMOCHEMICAL GAS-ANALYSIS APPARATUS, Zavodskaya Lab. 22, (6) 735-38 (1956); Anal. Abstr. 3, No. 3783 (1956).

316. Van Deempter, J. J. , Zuiderweg, F. J. and Klinkenberg, A.
     LONGITUDINAL DIFFUSION AND RESISTANCE TO MASS
     TRANSFER AS A CAUSE OF NON-IDEALITY IN CHROMA-
     TOGRAPHY, Chem. Eng. Sci. 5, 271 (1956).

317. Vandenheuvel, F. A. and Vatcher, D. R. PARTITION
     CHROMATOGRAPHY OF ALIPHATIC ACIDS, Anal. Chem.
     28, 838-45 (1956).

318. Vladimirov, B. V. APPARATUS FOR GAS ANALYSIS BY
     GAS CHROMATOGRAPHY, Neftyanoe Khoz. 34, (8), 61-64
     (1956); C. A. 51, 4061c (1957).

319. Wencke, K. CHROMATOGRAPHIC ANALYSIS OF MIX-
     TURES OF READILY VOLATILE GASES. Chem. Tech.
     (Berlin) 8, 728-30 (1956); C. A. 51, 11930 (1957).

320. Wherry, T. C. AUTOMATIC PROCESS STREAM ANALYZ-
     ERS. Oil Gas J. 54 (56), 125-26, 129 (1956).

321. Whitham, B. T. A LARGE SCALE ANALYTICAL GAS-
     LIQUID PARTITION CHROMATOGRAPHIC UNIT. See ref.
     365.

322. Whitham, B. T. APPLICATION OF GAS-LIQUID PARTI-
     TION CHROMATOGRAPHY TO SOLVENT ANALYSIS, See
     ref. 365.

323. Wiebe, A. K. ELUTION TIME AND RESOLUTION IN
     VAPOR CHROMATOGRAPHY, J. Phys. Chem. 60, 685-88
     (1956); C. A. 50, 12725 (1956).

324. Wirth, M. M. THE HYDROGEN MICROFLARE DETECTOR
     USING NITROGEN AS A CARRIER GAS, See ref. 365.

325. Wise, K. V. and Oliver, G. D. GAS CHROMATOGRAPHY.
     EFFECTS OF SOME OF THE VARIABLES ENCOUNTERED
     IN THE ELUTION TECHNIQUE AND SOME APPLICATIONS
     OF THE DISPLACEMENT TECHNIQUE, Presented at the
     Symp. on Vapor-Phase Chromatography, 129th Natl. ACS
     Meeting, Dallas, Texas, April 1956.

326. Wiseman, W. A. THE USE OF HELIUM AS THE MOBILE
     PHASE IN GAS CHROMATOGRAPHY, Chem. & Ind. (London)
     1956, 127-29.

327.   Zhukovitskii, A. A. and Turkeltaub, N. M.   CHROMATO-
       GRAPHIC METHOD OF SEPARATION AND ANALYSIS OF
       GASES. Uspekhi Khim. 25, 859-71 (1956);   C. A. 50, 15324
       (1956).

328.   Zhukovitskii, A. A. and Turkeltaub, N. M.   APPARATUS
       FOR THE CONTINUOUS ANALYSIS OF GASES.   Zavod-
       skaya Lab. 22, 1252-55 (1956);   C. A. 51, 13471 (1957).

                              1957

329.   Abraham, M. H. , Davies, A. G. , Llewellyn, D. R. and
       Thain, E. M.   CHROMATOGRAPHIC ANALYSIS OF
       ORGANIC PEROXIDES. Anal. Chim. Acta 17, 499-503(1957).

330.   Ahrens, R. W. , Sauer, M. C. , Jr. and Willard, J. E.
       HYDROGEN LABELLING OF HYDROCARBONS USING
       IONIZING RADIATION.   J. Am. Chem. Soc. 79, 3285(1957).

331.   Anderson, J. R. and Napier, K. H.   THERMODYNAMIC
       DATA FROM GAS-LIQUID PARTITION CHROMATOG-
       RAPHY. Australian J. Chem. 10, 250-55 (1957);   C. A. 51,
       17329 (1957).

332.   Andrychuk, D. , Edds, D. L. and Knapp, R. E.   GAS
       CHROMATOGRAPHIC ANALYSIS OF CHLORAL. Presented
       at the Pittsburgh Conf. on Anal. Chem. & Appl. Spec. ,
       March 1957; Appl. Spectroscopy 11, 102 (1957).

333.   Ashahara, T. and Takagi, Y. GAS CHROMATOGRAPHY.
       Abura Kagaku 6, 32-36, 108-112 (1957);   C. A. 51, 11810 (1957).

334.   Ashbury, G. K. , Davies, A. J. and Drinkwater, J. W.
       VERSATILE GAS-LIQUID PARTITION CHROMATOGRAPHY
       APPARATUS, Anal. Chem. 29, 918-25 (1957).

335.   Ayers, B. O.   CHROMATOGRAPHIC ANALYZERS IN PRO-
       CESS INSTRUMENTATION, See ref. 551.

336.   Baker, W. J. , Norlin, H. L. , Zinn, T. L. and Wall, R. F.
       DESIGN PARAMETERS FOR PROCESS GAS CHROMATO-
       GRAPHS, (Preprints) Div. Petrol Chem. ACS, Vol. 2,
       No. 4, D-43, New York, September 1957.

337.   Barefoot, R. R. and Currah, J. E.   GAS CHROMATOG-

GRAPHY. REVIEW OF RECENT PROGRESS, Chem. in Can. 9, (3) 68-72 (1957).

338. Barrer, R. M. and Hampton, M. G. GAS CHROMATOG-RAPHY AND MIXTURE ISOTHERMS IN ALKYL AMMONIUM BENTONITES, Trans. Faraday Soc. 53, 1462-75 (1957).

339. Bayer, E., Reuther, K. H. and Born, F. ANALYSIS OF AMINO-ACID MIXTURES BY GAS PARTITION CHROMA-TOGRAPHY, Angew. Chem. 69, 640 (1957).

340. Beaven, G. H., James, A. T. and Johnson, E. A. STERIC EFFECTS IN THE GAS-LIQUID CHROMATOGRAPHY OF SOME ALKYLBIPHENYLS, Nature 179, 490-91 (1957); C. A. 51, 11003c (1957).

341. Beckwith, A. L. J. and Waters, W. A. REACTION OF CHLOROBENZENE WITH METHYL RADICALS. J. Chem. Soc. 1957, 1665-68.

342. Beerthius, R. K. and Keppler, J. G. GAS CHROMATO-GRAPHIC ANALYSIS OF HIGHER FATTY ACIDS: UP TO AND INCLUDING CEROTIC ACID, Nature 179, 731-32 (1957); C. A. 51, 10313c (1957).

343. Benedek, P., Szepesy, L. and Szepe, S. THE CALCULA-TION OF THE CONTINUOUS CHROMATOGRAPHIC COL-UMN, See ref. 551.

344. Bernard, R. A. SEPARATION AND IDENTIFICATION OF SOME TERPENES BY GAS PARTITION CHROMATOGRA-PHIC ANALYSIS, J. Assoc. Offic. Agr. Chemists 40, 915-21 (1957).

345. Beroes, C. S. A CRITICAL STUDY OF THE VARIABLES AFFECTING RETENTION TIME AND RESOLUTION IN THE GAS-LIQUID CHROMATOGRAPHIC COLUMN, THESIS, University of Pittsburgh, June 1957.

346. Bohemen, J. and Purnell, J. H. KATHAROMETRIC MEASUREMENT OF THEORETICAL PLATE NUMBERS IN GAS CHROMATOGRAPHY, Chem. & Ind. (London) 1957, (25), 815-16.

347. Bishop, J.R., Liebmann, H. and Humphrey, M.   THE
     DETERMINATION OF HYDROGEN IN HEAD-SPACE
     GASES IN FOOD CANS BY GAS CHROMATOGRAPHY.
     Chem. & Ind. (London) 1957, 360-62.

348. Brenner, N.   GAS CHROMATOGRAPHY.   Drug and Cos-
     metic Ind. 80, 166-67, 261-66 (1957); C.A. 51, 9085 (1957).

349. Brenner, N.   SPECIAL APPLICATIONS OF GAS CHRO-
     MATOGRAPHY EQUIPMENT TO CHEMICAL LABORATORY
     PROBLEMS, Presented at Pittsburgh Conf. on Anal. Chem.
     & Appl. Spec., March 1957.

350. Brenner, N.   MODIFICATION OF A GAS CHROMATOG-
     RAPHY INSTRUMENT FOR SPECIAL LABORATORY
     PROBLEMS, Presented at Natl. ACS Meet., Miami, Florida,
     April 1957.

351. Browning, L.C. and Watts, J.O.   INTERPRETATION OF
     AREAS USED FOR QUANTITATIVE ANALYSIS IN GAS-
     LIQUID PARTITION CHROMATOGRAPHY.   Anal. Chem.
     29, 24-27 (1957).

352. Burrell Corp.   ADSORBENTS FOR CHROMATOGRAPHIC
     ANALYSIS, Bulletin No. 835, Pittsburgh, 1957.

353. Burrows, G.   PROCESS OF GAS-LIQUID CHROMATOG-
     RAPHY.   Trans. Inst. Chem. Engrs. (London) 35, 245
     (1957).

354. Carle, D.W.   PRECISE LIQUID SAMPLING IN GAS CHRO-
     MATOGRAPHY, August 1957.   See ref. 551.

355. Carson, J.F. and Wong, F.F.   GAS-LIQUID CHROMATOG-
     RAPHY OF THE VOLATILE COMPONENTS OF ONIONS,
     (Preprints) Div. Petrol. Chem. ACS. Vol. 2, No. 4, D-115,
     New York, September 1957.

356. Cassidy, H.C.   FUNDAMENTALS OF CHROMATOGRAPHY,
     Interscience Publishers, Inc., New York, 1957.

357. Chovin, P.   GAS-PHASE CHROMATOGRAPHY, Bull. soc.
     chim. France 1957, 83-101; C.A. 51, 6273i (1957) review.

358. Cowan, C.B. and Stirling, P.J.   THE SELECTION AND

OPERATION OF THERMISTORS FOR KATHAROMETERS,
See ref. 551.

359. Cuthbertson, F. and Musgrove, W. K. R. 1:1–DIHALOCY-
CLOHEXANES (USE OF PREPARATIVE SCALE GAS
CHROMATOGRAPHY), J. Appl. Chem. 7, 99-104 (1957).

360. Darby, P. W. and Kemball, C. INVESTIGATION OF RE-
ACTIONS ALONG THE CATALYST BED IN FLOW SYSTEMS
BY VAPOUR PHASE CHROMATOGRAPHY. PART I.
DECOMPOSITION OF METHANOL ON A COBALT FISCHER-
TROPSCH CATALYST, Trans. Faraday Soc. 53, 832-40
(1957).

361. Davis, R. E. and McCrea, J. M. LIQUID SAMPLE INLET
SYSTEM FOR GAS CHROMATOGRAPHS, Anal. Chem. 29,
1114-15 (1957).

362. Davis, R. E. and Schreiber, R. A. DOUBLE COLUMN
GAS CHROMATOGRAPHY. (ANALYSIS OF NONCONDEN-
SABLE AND LIGHT HYDROCARBON GASES BY A COM-
BINED GAS-LIQUID, GAS-SOLID CHROMATOGRAPH),
(Preprints) Div. Petrol. Chem. ACS, Vol. 2, No. 4, D-91,
New York, September 1957.

363. Day, E. A. , Forss, D. A. and Patton, S. FLAVOR AND
ODOR DEFECTS OF GAMMA-IRRADIATED SKIM MILK.
II. IDENTIFICATION OF VOLATILE COMPONENTS BY
GAS CHROMATOGRAPHY AND MASS SPECTROMETRY,
J. Dairy Sci. 40, 932-41 (1957).

364. Desty, D. H. VAPOUR DETECTORS FOR GAS CHROMA-
TOGRAPHY, Nature 180, 22-23 (1957).

365. Desty, D. H. VAPOUR PHASE CHROMATOGRAPHY.
Proceedings of the Symposium Sponsored by the Hydrocarbon Research Group of the Institute of Petroleum held
in London, May 1956; Academic Press, New York and
Butterworths Scientific Publications, London, 1957.

366. Desty, D. H. GAS CHROMATOGRAPHY, Nature 179,
241-42 (1957) - committee recommendations.

367. Desty, D. H. and Harbourn, C. L. A. AN EVALUATION
OF A COMMERCIAL ALKYL ARYL SULFONATE DETER-

GENT AS A COLUMN PACKING FOR GAS CHROMATOG-
RAPHY, (Preprints) Div. Petrol. Chem. ACS, Vol. 2,
No. 4, D-157, New York, September 1957.

368. Desty, D. H. and Whyman, B. H. F. APPLICATION OF
      GAS-LIQUID CHROMATOGRAPHY TO ANALYSIS OF
      LIQUID PETROLEUM FRACTIONS, Anal. Chem. 29,
      320-29 (1957).

369. Dewhurst, H. A. RADIATION CHEMISTRY OF ORGANIC
      COMPOUNDS. I. n-ALKANE LIQUIDS. (Use of Gas
      Chromatography). J. Phys. Chem. 61, 1466-71 (1957).

370. Dewhurst, H. A. and Winslow, E. H. ELECTRON AND
      GAMMA-RAY RADIOLYSIS OF n-HEXANE. (Use of Gas
      Chromatography). J. Chem. Phys. 26, 969-70 (1957).

371. Dietz, W. A. ANALYSIS OF LIGHT ENDS ON SATURATE
      NAPHTHAS, USING GAS CHROMATOGRAPHY, See ref. 551.

372. Dietz, W. A. and Dudenbostel, B. F. , Jr. APPLICATIONS
      OF GAS CHROMATOGRAPHY TO PETROLEUM PROCES-
      SES, (Preprints) Div. Petrol. Chem. ACS, Vol. 2, No. 4,
      D-171, New York, September 1957.

373. Dintenfass, H. T. SELECTIVE POLAR ADSORPTION.
      Chem. & Ind. (London) 1957, 560; Kolloid Z. 151, 154 (1957).

374. Dolphin, J. L. and Stanley, T. W. VAPOR PHASE CHRO-
      MATOGRAPHY IN AIR POLLUTION STUDIES. COLUMN
      EVALUATION, Presented at 131st Natl. ACS Meeting,
      Miami, Florida, April 1957.

375. Domange, L. and Longuevalle, S. ANALYSIS OF
      SCHLEICH'S ANAESTHETIC MIXTURE BY GAS-LIQUID
      PARTITION CHROMATOGRAPHY, Ann. Pharm. Franc.
      1957, 15 (7-8) 448-54.

376. Donner, W. ELECTRONICS CONTROLS GAS CHROMA-
      TOGRAPHY. Electronics 30, No. 11, 164-66 (1957).

377. Donner, W. , Johns, T. and Gallaway, W. S. USE OF A
      MASS SPECTROMETER AS A GAS CHROMATOGRAPH
      DETECTOR, Presented at meeting of ASTM Committee
      E-14 on Mass Spectrometry, New York, May 1957;

Abstracted in Anal. Chem. 29, 1378 (1957).

378. Dudenbostel, B. F. , Jr. and Skarstrom, C. W. GAS
CHROMATOGRAPHY FOR PLANT STREAM ANALYSIS.
ADVANCES IN GAS CHROMATOGRAPHY, Div. Petrol.
Chem. ACS, Vol. 2, No. 4, D-177, New York, September
1957.

379. Dykstra, S. and Mosher, H. S. ORGANIC PEROXIDES.
VI. ALLYL HYDROPEROXIDE. (Use of Gas Chromatography.) J. Am. Chem. Soc. 79, 3474-75 (1957).

380. Eastman, R. H. SEMI-QUANTITATIVE GAS CHROMA-
TOGRAPHY, J. Am. Chem. Soc. 79, 4243 (1957).

381. Eggertsen, F. T. and Groennings, S. DETERMINATION
OF FIVE-TO-SEVEN CARBON SATURATES BY GAS
CHROMATOGRAPHY. Presented at American Petroleum
Institute, Division of Petroleum Meeting, Philadelphia,
Pennsylvania, May 1957; Abstracted in Petrol. Refiner
36, (5), 205 (1957).

382. Esayan, L. and Esayan, M. CHROMATOGRAPHY OF
GASES. I. SEPARATION OF ACETYLENE-HYDROGEN-
METHANE MIXTURES, Rev. chim. min. ind. chim.
(Roumania) 8, 447-52 (1957).

383. Fawcett, J. S. and Taylor, B. W. A HIGH TEMPERATURE
GAS-CHROMATOGRAPHY APPARATUS, (Preprints) Div.
Petrol. Chem. ACS, Vol. 2, No. 4, D-85, New York,
September 1957.

384. Fellows, C. G. ANALYZE GAS AND VAPOR PRODUCTS
BY CHROMATOGRAPHIC MEANS, Control Eng. 4, 75
(1957).

385. Felton, H. R. A NOVEL HIGH TEMPERATURE GAS
CHROMATOGRAPHY UNIT, See ref. 551.

386. Friedrich, K. PARTITION OF METHYLCHLOROSILANES
BY GAS-LIQUID CHROMATOGRAPHY, Chem. & Ind.
(London) 1957, 47.

387. Gallaway, W. S. and Johns, T. INVESTIGATION OF THE
COMBINED USE OF MASS SPECTROSCOPY AND GAS

CHROMATOGRAPHY. Presented at Pittsburgh Conf. on
Anal. Chem. and Appl. Spec., March 1957.

388. Gault, F.G., Germain, J.J. and Conia, J. THE METHYL-
ATION OF CYCLOPENTANONES. (Use of Gas Chromatography). Bull. soc. chim, France 1064-69 (1957).

389. Gil-Av, E, Herling, J. and Shabtai, J. GAS-LIQUID
PARTITION CHROMATOGRAPHY OF MIXTURES OF THE
THREE ISOMERIC METHYLCYCLOHEXENES AND METH-
YLENECYCLOHEXANE, Chem. & Ind. (London) 1957,
1483-84.

390. Gjaldbaek, J.C. GAS CHROMATOGRAPHY. Dansk Tidskr.
Farm. 31, 225-40 (1957).

391. Gohlke, R.S. INSTRUMENT DESIGN FOR GAS–LIQUID
PARTITION CHROMATOGRAPHY, Anal. Chem. 29,
1723-24 (1957).

392. Gohlke, R.S. THE USE OF TIME OF FLIGHT MASS
SPECTROMETRY AND VAPOR PHASE CHROMATOG-
RAPHY IN THE IDENTIFICATION OF UNKNOWN MIX-
TURES, (Preprints) Div. Petrol. Chem. ACS. Vol. 2,
No. 4, D-77, New York, September 1957.

393. Golay, M.J.E. VAPOR PHASE CHROMATOGRAPHY AND
THE TELEGRAPHER'S EQUATION, Anal. Chem. 29,
928-32 (1957).

394. Golay, M.J.E. A PERFORMANCE INDEX FOR GAS
CHROMATOGRAPHIC COLUMNS, Nature 180, 435 (1957).

395. Golay, M.J.E. THEORY AND PRACTICE OF GAS-LIQUID
PARTITION CHROMATOGRAPHY WITH COATED CAPIL-
LARIES, See ref. 551.

396. Gordon, R.J. and Moore, R.J. IDENTIFICATION OF
AROMATIC TYPES IN A HEAVILY CRACKED GAS OIL,
Presented at Pittsburgh Conf. on Anal. Chem. & Appl.
Spec., March 1957.

397. Gordus, A.A. and Willard, J.E. GAS PHASE REACTIONS
ACTIVATED BY NUCLEAR PROCESSES. (Use of Gas
Chromatography), J. Am. Chem. Soc. 79, 4609-16 (1957).

398. Gray, F.B. NEW ANALYTICAL TECHNIQUES FOR
      MEASUREMENT OF HYDROCARBON GASES IN DRILL-
      ING MUDS, Presented at Pittsburgh Conf. on Anal. Chem.
      & Appl. Spec., March 1957.

399. Green, G.E. A HYDROGEN CONVERSION DETECTOR
      FOR GAS CHROMATOGRAPHY, Nature 180, 295-96 (1957).

400. Greene, S.A. THE APPLICATIONS OF GAS ADSORPTION
      CHROMATOGRAPHY TO THE ANALYSIS OF CHEMICAL
      REACTIONS IN FLOW SYSTEMS, J. Chem. Educ. 34,
      194-95 (1957).

401. Greene, S.A. CALCULATION OF THE LIMITING RETEN-
      TION VOLUME IN GAS-LIQUID PARTITION CHROMATOG-
      RAPHY, J. Phys. Chem. 61, 702 (1957).

402. Greene, S.A. THE SEPARATION OF THE RARE GASES
      BY GAS-SOLID CHROMATOGRAPHY, (Preprints) Div.
      Petrol. Chem. ACS, Vol. 2, No. 4, D-105, New York,
      September 1957.

403. Greene, S.A. and Pust, H. USE OF SILICA GEL AND
      ALUMINA IN GAS-ADSORPTION CHROMATOGRAPHY,
      Anal. Chem. 29, 1055 (1957).

404. Greene, S.A. and Pust, H. THE ANALYSIS OF NITROGEN
      DIOXIDE BY GAS-SOLID CHROMATOGRAPHY. Advances
      in Gas Chromatography (Preprints) Div. Petrol. Chem.
      ACS, Vol. 2, No. 4, D-107, New York, September 1957.

405. Greene, S.A. and Roy, H.E. EFFECT OF DIFFERENT
      CARRIER GASES ON RETENTION TIMES IN GAS-AD—
      SORPTION CHROMATOGRAPHY, Anal. Chem. 29, 569-70
      (1957).

406. Gygi, R. and Potterat, M. APPLICATIONS OF GAS
      CHROMATOGRAPHY, Mitt. Gebiete Lebensm. u. Hyg. 48,
      497-504 (1957).

407. Hall, W.K. and Emmett, P.H. AN IMPROVED MICRO-
      CATALYTIC TECHNIQUE, J. Am. Chem. Soc. 79, 2091-
      2093 (1957).

408. Hall, W.K., Sill, G. and Wolfe, C.L. INTEGRATING

DEVICE FOR USE WITH POTENTIOMETERS. Science
126, 821-23 (1957).

409. Harva, O. and Keltakallio, A. CHROMATOGRAPHIC
DETERMINATION OF ARGON IN GAS ANALYSIS. Suomen
Kemistilehti 30B, 223-24 (1957).

410. Haslam, T. and Jeffs, A. R. GAS-LIQUID CHROMATOG-
RAPHY IN A PLASTICS ANALYTICAL LABORATORY,
J. Appl. Chem. 7, 24-32 (1957).

411. Hasselstrom, T. FRUIT AND VEGETABLE FLAVORS -
TECHNIQUES EMPLOYED IN THE STUDY OF THE
CHEMISTRY OF CABBAGE FLAVOR, Quartermaster Food
and Container Inst. Surveys Progr. Military Subsistence
Problems, Ser. I., No. 9, 76-86 (1957).

412. Hatch, L. F. THE USE OF GAS CHROMATOGRAPHY IN
KINETIC STUDIES, See ref. 551.

413. Hausdorff, H. H. QUANTITATIVE METHODS FOR GAS
CHROMATOGRAPHY, Chemiker Ztg. 81, 392-96 (1957).

414. Hawkes, J. C. THE FATTY ACIDS OF BUTTERFAT AND
THE VOLATILE ACIDS FORMED ON OXIDATION, J.
Dairy Res. 24, 366-71 (1957).

415. Hawkes, J. C., Dunkley, W. S. and Hooker, C. N. THE
SEPARATION OF FATTY ESTERS AND ALDEHYDES BY
GAS LIQUID CHROMATOGRAPHY, New Zealand J. of
Science and Technology 38, Sec. B, No. 9, 925-38 (1957).

416. Heilbronner, I. E., Kovats, E. and Simon, W. PROGRAM-
CONTROLLED GAS CHROMATOGRAPHY FOR PREPARA-
TIVE SEPARATION OF ORGANIC COMPOUNDS, Helv.
Chim. Acta 40, 2410-20 (1957).

417. Heines, Sister Virginia, Juhasz, Sister R., O'Leary,
Sister Adeline and Schramm, Guenter, GAS CHROMA-
TOGRAPHY OF C_2 TO C_{11} FATTY ACIDS WITH SIMPLI-
FIED APPARATUS, Trans. Kentucky Acad. Sci. 18, 1-7
(1957).

418. Helms, C. C. and Claudy, H. N. THE PRACTICAL DE-
SIGN OF A VAPOR FRACTOMETER FOR AUTOMATIC

MULTI-COMPONENT ANALYSIS OF PROCESS STREAMS,
See ref. 551.

419. Helms, C. C. and Norem, S. A LOOK AT VAPOR-PHASE
      CHROMATOGRAPHY. Oil Gas J. 55 (17), 146-49 (1957);
      C. A. 51, 13367 (1957).

420. Hendricks, W. J., Soemantri, R. M. and Waterman, H. I.
      THE SEPARATION OF MIXTURES OF BIPHENYL, CYCLO-
      HEXYLBENZENE AND BICYCLOHEXYL BY VAPOUR-
      PHASE CHROMATOGRAPHY. J. Inst. Petrol. 43, 288-91
      (1957).

421. Hodgmen, C. D. HANDBOOK OF CHEMISTRY AND PHYS-
      ICS, Chemical Rubber Publishing Co., Cleveland, Ohio
      1957.

422. Holmes, J. C. and Morrell, F. A. OSCILLOGRAPHIC
      MASS-SPECTROMETRIC MONITORING OF GAS CHRO-
      MATOGRAPHY. Appl. Spectroscopy 11, 86-87 (1957);
      C. A. 51, 14329 (1957).

423. Horn, O., Schwenk, U. and Hachenberg, H. GAS CHRO-
      MATOGRAPHY, Brennstoff-Chem. 38, 116-20 (1957);
      C. A. 51, 10177h (1957).

424. Howard, G. A. and Slater, C. A. HYDROCARBONS OF
      THE ESSENTIAL OIL FROM HOPS, Chem. & Ind. (London)
      1957, 495.

425. Insull, W., Jr. and James, A. T. THE QUANTITATIVE
      AND QUALITATIVE ANALYSIS OF FATTY ACIDS IN THE
      RANGE C_1 TO C_{20}, (Preprints) Div. Petrol. Chem. ACS,
      Vol. 2, No. 4, D-111, New York, September 1957.

426. Jacobs, M. B. COMPOSITION OF ONION OIL, Am. Per-
      fumer Aromat. 70, (5), 53-56 (1957).

427. James, A. T. SEPARATION AND IDENTIFICATION OF
      SATURATED AND UNSATURATED FATTY ACIDS FROM
      FORMIC ACID TO DODECANOIC ACID BY GAS CHROMA-
      TOGRAPHY, Fette u. Seifen 59, 73-77 (1957).

428. James, A. T. and Webb, J. DETERMINATION OF STRUC-
      TURE OF UNSATURATED FATTY ACIDS ON A MICRO-

SCALE WITH THE GAS-LIQUID CHROMATOGRAM,
Biochem. J. 66, 515-20 (1957).

429. Janak, J. NEW WAYS OF GAS ANALYSIS BY GAS CHRO-
MATOGRAPHY, Erdöl u. Kohle 10, 442-44 (1957).

430. Janak, J., Nedorost, M. and Bubenikova, V. CHROMA-
TOGRAPHIC SEMIMICROANALYSIS OF GASES. XIII.
SEPARATION OF CHLORINE, BROMINE AND IODINE,
Chem. listy 51, 890-94 (1957); C.A. 51, 11924 (1957).

431. Janak, J. and Novak, J. CHROMATOGRAPHIC SEMI-
MICROANALYSIS OF GASES. XIV. DIRECT DETER-
MINATION OF INDIVIDUAL GASEOUS PARAFFINS AND
OLEFINS IN BUTA-1, 3-DIENE. Chem. listy 51, 1832-37
(1957).

432. Jennings, W.G. APPLICATION OF GAS-LIQUID PARTI-
TION CHROMATOGRAPHY TO THE STUDY OF VOLATILE
FLAVOR COMPOUNDS, J. Dairy Sci. 40, 271-79 (1957);
C.A. 51, 10789 (1957).

433. Johns, T. THE BEHAVIOR OF THE SOLID SUPPORT IN
GAS-LIQUID PARTITION CHROMATOGRAPHY, See ref.
551.

434. Johnson, E.A. THE DIMETHYLDIPHENYLS, J. Chem.
Soc. 1957, 4155-56.

435. Jones, W.C., Jr. THE ANALYSIS OF C_6 - C_9 AROMAT-
ICS BY GAS-LIQUID PARTITION CHROMATOGRAPHY,
(Preprints) Div. Petrol. Chem. ACS, Vol. 2, No. 4, D-117,
New York, September 1957.

436. Juranek, J. COMBINED COLORIMETRIC AND CHROMA-
TOGRAPHIC ULTRAMICRO ANALYSIS OF GASES. I.
ANALYSIS OF COMPOUNDS FORMING CARBON DIOXIDE
ON COMBUSTION, Chem. listy 51, 2280-86 (1957).

437. Kaufman, J.J., Todd, J.E. and Koski, W.S. APPLICA-
TION OF GAS PHASE CHROMATOGRAPHY TO THE BORON
HYDRIDES, Anal. Chem. 29, 1032-35 (1957).

438. Kebarle, P. and Bryce, W.A. THE DECOMPOSITION OF
1-BUTENE AND 1-BUTENE-4 d_3 INDUCED BY METHYL

RADICALS. Can. J. Chem. 35, 576-79 (1957).

439. Keulemans, A.I.M. GAS CHROMATOGRAPHY, Reinhold Publishing Corp., New York 1957.

440. Keulemans, A.I.M. SOME FUNDAMENTAL ASPECTS OF GAS CHROMATOGRAPHY, (Preprints) Div. Petrol. Chem. ACS, Vol. 2, No. 4, D-5, New York, September 1957.

441. Keulemans, A.I.M., Kwantes, A. and Rijnders, G.W.A. QUANTITATIVE ANALYSIS WITH THERMAL CONDUC-TIVITY DETECTION IN GAS-LIQUID CHROMATOGRAPHY, Anal. Chim. Acta 16, 29-39 (1957); C.A. 51, 7931i (1957).

442. Kirkland, J.J. AN APPARATUS FOR LABORATORY PREPARATIVE-SCALE VAPOR PHASE CHROMATOG-RAPHY, See ref. 551.

443. Kjaer, A. and Jart, A. iso-THIOCYANATES. XXIX. SEPARATION OF VOLATILE iso-THIOCYANATES BY GAS CHROMATOGRAPHY. Acta Chem. Scand. 11, 1423 (1957).

444. Knox, J.H. GAS CHROMATOGRAPHY, Sci. Prog. 45, 227 (1957); C.A. 51, 9398 (1957).

445. Kögler, H. THERMO-GAS-CHROMATOGRAPHY, A NEW METHOD FOR THE SEPARATION AND DETERMINATION OF MIXTURES, Chem. Tech. (Berlin) 9, 400-03(1957).

446. Kögler, H., Hultschig, M., Fischer, J. and Weidenbach, G. AUTOMATIC GAS ANALYSIS IN INDUSTRIAL CONTROL, Chem. Tech. (Berlin) 9, 220 (1957); C.A. 51, 13359 (1957).

447. Kyryacos, G. and Boord, C.E. GAS ADSORPTION CHRO-MATOGRAPHY IN THE ANALYSIS OF COOL-FLAME COM-BUSTION PRODUCTS, Presented at 131st Natl. ACS Meet-ing, Miami, Florida, April 1957.

448. Kyryacos, G. and Boord, C.E. SEPARATION OF HYDRO-GEN, OXYGEN, NITROGEN, METHANE, AND CARBON MONOXIDE BY GAS ADSORPTION CHROMATOGRAPHY, Anal. Chem. 29, 787-88 (1957).

449. Lederer, E. and Lederer, M. CHROMATOGRAPHY. A

REVIEW OF PRINCIPLES AND APPLICATIONS, D. Van
Nostrand Company, Inc., Princeton, New Jersey, 1957.

450. Leibnitz, E., Hrapia, H. and Könnecke, H. G. AN INTE-
      GRAL-DETECTOR FOR CHROMATOGRAPHIC GAS ANALY-
      SIS, Brennstoff-Chem. 38, 14-16 (1957); C. A. 51, 4877d
      (1957).

451. Leithe, W. PRACTICAL APPLICATIONS OF GAS CHRO-
      MATOGRAPHY, Österr. Chem. -Ztg. 58, 141-48 (1957);
      C. A. 51, 16191 (1957).

452. Liberti, A. COULOMETRY APPLIED TO GAS-PHASE
      CHROMATOGRAPHY, Anal. Chim. Acta 17, 247-53 (1957);
      C. A. 51, 12733f (1957).

453. Lewis, J. S. and Patton, H. W. ANALYSIS OF ESTER-TYPE
      PLASTICIZERS BY GAS-LIQUID CHROMATOGRAPHY.
      See ref. 551.

454. Madden, W. F., Quigg, R. K. and Kemball, C. A METHOD
      OF IMPROVING THE NULL-POINT OF THERMAL CON-
      DUCTIVITY CELLS FOR GAS-LIQUID CHROMATOGRAPHY,
      Chem. & Ind. (London) 1957, 892; C. A. 51, 14329 (1957).

455. Marechal, J. INTRODUCTION TO VAPOR PHASE CHRO-
      MATOGRAPHY. Ind. Chim. belge 22 (6), 675 (1957).

456. Martin, A. J. P. PAST, PRESENT AND FUTURE OF GAS
      CHROMATOGRAPHY, See ref. 551.

457. Maurel, R. EXPERIMENTAL PRECISION IN QUANTITA-
      TIVE ANALYSIS BY GAS CHROMATOGRAPHY, Compt.
      rend. 244, 3157-59 (1957).

458. McCreadie, S. W. S. and Williams, A. F. THE QUANTITA-
      TIVE MEASUREMENT AND TRANSFER OF SAMPLES IN
      GAS CHROMATOGRAPHY, J. Appl. Chem. 7, 47 (1957);
      C. A. 51, 13471 (1957).

459. Menapace, H. R., Kyryacos, G. and Boord, C. E. GAS
      ADSORPTION CHROMATOGRAPHIC DETERMINATION OF
      SOME OXYGENATED PRODUCTS IN COOL-FLAME COM-
      BUSTION, (Preprints) Div. Petrol. Chem. ACS, Vol. 2,
      No. 4, D-153, New York, September 1957.

460. Meyer, R.A. ROUTINE GAS CHROMATOGRAPHIC ANALY-
SIS FOR TRACE MATERIALS, Presented at the Pittsburgh
Conf. on Anal. Chem. & Appl. Spec., March 1957.

461. Meyer, R.A. THE ANALYSIS OF HIGH VAPOR PRESSURE
NATURAL GASOLINES, See ref. 551.

462. Moghadame, P.E. CHROMATOGRAPHIC SEPARATION
IN THE VAPOUR PHASE, Rev. ins. franc. petrole 12,
58 (1957).

463. Monkman, J.L. SOME APPLICATIONS OF GAS CHROMA-
TOGRAPHY TO COMMONLY ENCOUNTERED ANALYTICAL
PROBLEMS, See ref. 551.

464. Morrow, H.N. and Buckley, K.B. NEED HELP WITH
GAS CHROMATOGRAPHY ?, Petrol. Refiner 36 (8), 157
(1957).

465. Müller, R.H. INSTRUMENTATION: VAPOR PHASE
CHROMATOGRAPHY USED TO PERFORM AUTOMATIC
ANALYSES, Anal. Chem. 29 (3), 55A-57A (1957); ibid.
29 (10), 67A-68A (1957).

466. Munch, R.H. VAPOR PHASE CHROMATOGRAPHY.
Record Chem. Progr. (Kresge-Hooker Sci. Lib.) 18,
69-101 (1957); C.A. 51, 12598 (1957).

467. Nogare, S. Dal, Bennett, C.E. and Harden, J.C.
A SIMPLE ELECTROMECHANICAL INTEGRATOR. See
ref. 551.

468. Norem, S.D. A COMBUSTION DEVICE FOR USE IN
CONJUNCTION WITH CHROMATOGRAPHIC COLUMNS,
See ref. 551.

469. Norris, T.G. and Crosser, O.K. NON-IDEAL EFFECTS
UPON ELUTION CURVE SHAPE IN VAPOR PARTITION
CHROMATOGRAPHY, (Preprints) Div. Petrol. Chem.
ACS, Vol. 2, No. 4, D-15, New York, September 1957.

470. Nowakowska, J., Melvin, E.H. and Wiebe, R. SEPARA-
TION OF THE OXIDATION PRODUCTS OF FATTY ACIDS
BY MEANS OF GAS-LIQUID PARTITION CHROMATOG-
RAPHY. J. Am. Oil Chemists' Soc. 34, 411-14 (1957);
C.A. 51, 15149 (1957).

471. Nunez, L. J., Armstrong, W. H. and Cogswell, H. W.
      ANALYSIS OF HYDROCARBON BLENDS BY GAS-LIQUID
      PARTITION CHROMATOGRAPHY, Anal. Chem. 29, 1164-
      1165 (1957).

472. Nuttall, R. L. and Ginnings, D. C. THERMAL CONDUC-
      TIVITY OF NITROGEN FROM 50° TO 500°C and 1 TO 100
      ATMOSPHERES, J. Research NBS 58, 271-78 (1957).

473. Ober, S. S. THE INTERRELATIONSHIP OF COLUMN
      EFFICIENCY AND RESOLVING POWER IN GAS CHROMA-
      TOGRAPHY, See ref. 551.

474. Parsons, T. D., Silverman, M. B. and Ritter, D. M.
      ALKENYLBORANES. I. PREPARATION AND PROPER-
      TIES OF SOME VINYL AND PROPENYLBORANES, J. Am.
      Chem. Soc. 79, 5091-5101 (1957).

475. Percival, W. C. QUANTITATIVE DETERMINATION OF
      FLUORINATED HYDROCARBONS BY GAS CHROMATOG-
      RAPHY, Anal. Chem. 29, 20-24 (1957).

476. Peyrot, P. USE OF VAPOR-PHASE CHROMATOGRAPHY
      FOR RAPID ANALYSIS OF MIXTURES OF SOLVENTS,
      Chem. & Ind. (Paris), 78, 3-8 (1957).

477. Phillips, C. GAS-LIQUID CHROMATOGRAPHY, Svensk.
      Kem. Tidskr. 69, 199 (1957); C. A. 51, 11809 (1957).

478. Phillips, C. GAS CHROMATOGRAPHY INSTRUMENTA-
      TION FOR THE LABORATORY, See ref. 551.

479. Pollard, F. H. and Hardy, C. J. THE ANALYSES OF
      HALOGENATED HYDROCARBONS BY VAPOUR PHASE
      CHROMATOGRAPHY, Anal. Chim. Acta 16, 135-43 (1957);
      C. A. 51, 7239d (1957).

480. Ray, N. H. GAS CHROMATOGRAPHY, Nature 180, 403
      (1957).

481. Rigby, F. L. and Bethune, J. L. ANALYSIS OF HOP OIL
      BY GAS LIQUID PARTITION CHROMATOGRAPHY. J.
      Inst. Brewing 63, 154-61 (1957).

482. Ring, R. D. THE EFFECT OF THE RATIO OF PARTITION

LIQUID TO INERT SUPPORT ON THE SEPARATION OF
(1) MONO-, DI-, AND TRIETHYLENE GLYCOLS AND
(2) CIS AND TRANS-2-5-DIMETHYLPIPERAZINE, See
ref. 551.

483. Rippere, R.E. ISOLATION AND IDENTIFICATION OF A
LOW CONCENTRATION COMPONENT BY GAS CHROMA-
TOGRAPHY AND MASS SPECTROMETRY, See ref. 551.

484. Root, M.J. QUALITY CONTROL OF CHLOROFLUORO-
METHANES AND CHLOROFLUOROETHANES BY GAS
CHROMATOGRAPHY, See ref. 551.

485. Root, M.J. and Maury, M.J. GAS-CHROMATOGRAPHIC
ANALYSIS OF AEROSOL PRODUCTS, J. Soc. Cosmetic
Chemists 8, 92-107 (1957); C.A. 51, 9095 (1957).

486. Rosie, D.M. and Grob, R.L. THERMAL CONDUCTIVITY
BEHAVIOR. IMPORTANCE IN QUANTITATIVE GAS CHRO-
MATOGRAPHY, Anal. Chem. 29, 1263-64 (1957).

487. Rowlinson, J.S. and Thacker, R. THE PHYSICAL PROP-
ERTIES AND SOME FLUORINE COMPOUNDS AND THEIR
SOLUTIONS. Trans. Faraday Soc. 53, 1-8 (1957).

488. Russell, D.S. and Bednas, M.E. TRANSFER CELL FOR
GAS CHROMATOGRAPHY, Anal. Chem. 29, 1562 (1957).

489. Ryce, S.A. and Bryce, W.A. IONIZATION GAUGE
DETECTOR FOR GAS CHROMATOGRAPHY, Nature 179,
541 (1957).

490. Ryce, S.A. and Bryce, W.A. IONIZATION GAUGE
DETECTOR FOR GAS CHROMATOGRAPHY, Can. J. Chem.
35, 1293-97 (1957).

491. Ryce, S.A. and Bryce, W.A. ANALYSIS OF VOLATILE
ORGANIC SULFUR COMPOUNDS BY GAS PARTITION
CHROMATOGRAPHY, Anal. Chem. 29, 925-28 (1957).

492₀ Ryce, S.A., Kebarle, P. and Bryce, W.A. THERMAL
CONDUCTIVITY CELL FOR GAS CHROMATOGRAPHY,
Anal. Chem. 29, 1386-87 (1957).

493. Schamp, N. GAS CHROMATOGRAPHY, Mededel. Vlaam.

Chem. Ver. 19, 53 (1957).

494. Scott, R. P. W. and Cheshire, J. D. HIGH-EFFICIENCY
COLUMNS FOR THE ANALYSIS OF HYDROCARBONS BY
GAS-LIQUID CHROMATOGRAPHY, Nature 180, 702-03
(1957).

495. Sekerka, B., Spevak, A. and Friedrich, K. INFRARED
INDICATION IN GAS CHROMATOGRAPHY. Chem.
prumysl. 7, 602-4 (1957).

496. Seligman, R. B., Resnik, F. E., O'Keefe, A., Holmes,
J. C., Morrell, F. A., Murrill, D. P. and Gager, F. L., Jr.
GAS CHROMATOGRAPHY IN TOBACCO RESEARCH.
Tobacco Sci. 1, 124-29, published in Tobacco 145, No. 9,
145, No. 9, 24-29 (1957).

497. Smith, R. P. and Tatlow, J. C. FLUOROCYCLOHEXANES.
(Use of Gas Chromatography). J. Chem. Soc. 1957, 2505-11.

498. Soemantri, R. M. and Waterman, H. I. SEPARATION OF
NAPHTHALENE AND ITS HYDROGENATED PRODUCTS
BY VAPOUR-PHASE CHROMATOGRAPHY, J. Inst. Petrol.
43, 94-99 (1957); C. A. 51, 7239f (1957).

499. Sokol, L. GAS-ADSORPTION CHROMATOGRAPHY WITH
THERMAL CONDUCTIVITY INDICATION, Chem. prumsyl.
7, 189 (1957).

500. Spacklen, S. B. THE DEVELOPMENT OF GAS CHROMATO-
GRAPHS. Instr. Soc. Am. J. 4, 514-17 (1957).

501. Stahl, W. H.   TECHNIQUES AND METHODS FOR RE-
SEARCH IN FLAVORS - GAS CHROMATOGRAPHY AND
MASS SPECTROMETRY IN THE STUDY OF FLAVOR,
Quartermaster Food and Container Inst. Surveys Progr.
Military Subsistence Problems, Ser. I., No. 9, 58-76
(1957).

502. Straten, H. A. C. van. CHROMATOGRAPHIC GAS ANALY-
SIS. Chem. en Pharm. Tech. (Dordrecht) 12, 6 (1957).

503. Szulczewski, D. H. and Higuchi, T. GAS CHROMATO-
GRAPHIC SEPARATION OF SOME PERMANENT GASES
ON SILICA GEL AT REDUCED TEMPERATURES, Anal.

Chem. 29, 1541-43 (1957).

504. Taylor, B. W.   AN INSTRUMENT DESIGNED FOR HIGH
TEMPERATURE GAS CHROMATOGRAPHIC ANALYSIS,
See ref. 551.

505. Taylor, G. W. and Dunlop, A. S.   THE ANALYSIS OF LIGHT
HYDROCARBONS BY GAS-LIQUID CHROMATOGRAPHY.
See ref. 551.

506. Teitelbaum, C. L.   GAS-PARTITION CHROMATOGRAPHY.
APPLICATIONS TO ESSENTIAL OILS AND OTHER VOLA-
TILE MATERIALS, J. Soc. Cosmetic Chemists 8, 316-27
(1957).

507. Tenney, H. M. and Harris, R. J.   SAMPLE INTRODUCTION
SYSTEM FOR GAS CHROMATOGRAPHY, Anal. Chem. 29,
317-18 (1957).

508. Toth, J. and Graf, L.   ADSORPTION THEORY OF GAS
CHROMATOGRAPHY, Magyar Kem. Folyoirat 63, 71-73
(1957) in Hungarian with German Summary.

509. Turkeltaub, N. M.   A DISTRIBUTIONAL CHROMATO-
GRAPHIC TECHNIQUE FOR THE SEPARATION AND
DETERMINATION OF HYDROCARBON GASES. Zhur. Fiz.
Khim. 31, 2102-09 (1957).

510. Turowska, A. and Jedrzejczyk, B.   CHROMATOGRAPHIC
DETERMINATION OF ETHYLENE IN COAL GAS.   Gaz.
Woda i. Tech. Sanit. 31, 229-33, 266-69 (1957); C. A. 51,
18551 (1957).

511. Voss, G. and Hessenauer, F.   CHROMATOGRAPHY OF
GASES AND VAPORS, Erdöl u. Kohle 10, 161-63 (1957);
C. A. 51, 10177g (1957) - survey.

512. Walker, R. E. and Westenberg, A. A.   PRECISION THER-
MAL-CONDUCTIVITY GAS ANALYZER USING THERMIS-
TORS. Rev. Sci. Instr. 28, 789-92 (1957).

513. Warren, G. W. , Haskin, J. F. , Kourey, R. E. and Yar-
borough, V. A.   GAS CHROMATOGRAPHY. ANALYSIS
OF THE CRUDE REACTION PRODUCT FROM THE
HYDROFORMYLATION OF ISOBUTANE, (Preprints) Div.

Petrol. Chem. ACS, Vol. 2, No. 4, D-131, New York, September 1957.

514.   Weinstein, A.   FRACTION CUTTER FOR GAS CHROMA-TOGRAPHY.   Anal. Chem. $\underline{29}$, 1899 (1957).

515.   Wencke, K.   CHROMATOGRAPHIC METHOD FOR QUAN-TITATIVE GAS ANALYSIS, Chem. Tech. (Berlin) $\underline{9}$, 404-06 (1957).

516.   Whatmough, P.   DETERMINATION OF HYDROGEN IN MINE AIRS USING A GAS CHROMATOGRAPHIC TECH-NIQUE, Nature $\underline{179}$, 911 (1957).

517.   Wheatley, V.R. and James, A.T.   STUDIES OF SEBUM Biochem. J. $\underline{65}$, 36-42 (1957).

518.   White, D.   USE OF ORGANIC-MONTMORILLONITE COM-POUNDS IN GAS CHROMATOGRAPHY, Nature $\underline{179}$, 1075-76 (1957).

519.   Wilzbach, K.E. and Riesz, P.   ISOTOPE EFFECTS IN GAS-LIQUID CHROMATOGRAPHY, Science $\underline{126}$, 748-49, 1062 (1957).

520.   Wiseman, W.A.   BEHAVIOUR OF KATHAROMETERS. Chem. & Ind. (London) $\underline{1957}$, 1356-57.

521.   Young, J.F.   A DERIVATION OF THE EQUATION FOR ELUTION CHROMATOGRAPHY ASSUMING LINEAR RATE CONSTANTS,   See ref. 551.

522.   Zinn, T.L., Baker, W.J., Norlin, H.L. and Wall, R.F. EXPLORATORY PROCESS GAS CHROMATOGRAPHY, See ref. 551.

523.   Zlatkis, A.   THE RESOLUTION OF ISOMERIC HEXANES BY GAS-LIQUID CHROMATOGRAPHY, (Preprints) Div. Petrol. Chem. ACS, Vol. 2, No. 4, D-127, New York, September 1957.

524.   Zmitko, J., Brodsky, J. and Biza, V.   AUTOMATIC DEVICE FOR GAS CHROMATOGRAPHIC ANALYSIS, Chem. Tech. (Berlin) $\underline{9}$, 458-59 (1957).

525. Zmitko, J. , Brodsky, J. and Biza, V. AUTOMATIC
RECORDER OF GAS CHROMATOGRAPHIC ANALYSIS.
Chem. prumsyl. 7, 414-16 (1957).

                          1958

526. Adlard, E. R. and Whitham, B. T. APPLICATIONS OF
HIGH TEMPERATURE GAS-LIQUID CHROMATOGRAPHY
IN THE PETROLEUM INDUSTRY, See ref. 556.

527. Amberg, C. H. GAS-LIQUID PARTITION CHROMATOG-
RAPHY OF ORGANIC SULFUR COMPOUNDS, Can. J.
Chem. 36, 590-92 (1958).

528. Ambrose, D. and Purnell, J. H. THE PRESENTATION
OF GAS-LIQUID CHROMATOGRAPHIC RETENTION DATA.
PART II. , See ref. 556.

529. Ambrose, D. A. , Keulemans, A. I. M. and Purnell, J. H.
PRESENTATION OF GAS-LIQUID CHROMATOGRAPHIC
RETENTION DATA, Anal. Chem. 30, 1582 (1958).

530. Atkinson, A. P. and Tuey, G. A. P. AN AUTOMATIC
"PREPARATIVE-SCALE" GAS CHROMATOGRAPHY
APPARATUS, See ref. 556.

531. Baker, W. J. and Wall, R. F. COMPARATIVE STUDIES
OF GAS CHROMATOGRAPH COLUMN PARAMETERS,
ISA Proceedings; 1958 Natl. Symp. on Instrumental Methods
of Analysis, Houston, Texas, May 1958.

532. Baker, W. J. , Zinn, T. L. , Wise, K. V. and Wall, R. F.
OBSERVATIONS ON THE ANOMALOUS CHROMATOGRAPH-
IC BEHAVIOR OF HYDROGEN, ISA Proceedings; 1958 Natl.
Symp. on Instrumental Methods of Analysis, Houston, Texas,
May 1958.

533. Bayer, E. SEPARATION OF DERIVATIVES OF AMINO
ACIDS USING GAS-LIQUID CHROMATOGRAPHY,   See
ref. 556.

534. Bednas, M. E. and Russell, D. S. A STUDY OF SILVER
NITRATE SOLUTIONS IN GAS CHROMATOGRAPHY. Can.
J. Chem. 36, 1272-76 (1958).

535.   Bennett, C. E. , Nogare, S. Dal, Safranski, L. W. and
       Lewis, C. D.   TRACE ANALYSES BY GAS CHROMATOG-
       RAPHY, Anal. Chem. 30, 898 (1958).

536.   Benson, G. W. , Cowan, C. B. and Stirling, P. H. A THEO-
       RETICAL TREATMENT OF THE SENSITIVITY OF KATHAR-
       OMETERS, ISA Proceedings; 1958 Natl. Symp. on Instru-
       mental Methods of Analysis, Houston, Texas, May 1958.

537.   Benyon, J. H. , Clough, S. , Crooks, D. A. and Lester, G. R.
       A THEORY OF THE GAS-LIQUID CHROMATOGRAPHIC
       PROCESS. Trans. Faraday Soc. 54, 705-14 (1958).

538.   Bodnar, S. J. and Mayeux, S. J.   ESTIMATION OF TRACE
       AND MAJOR QUANTITIES OF LOWER ALCOHOLS,
       ETHERS, AND ACETONE IN AQUEOUS SOLUTION BY
       GAS LIQUID PARTITION CHROMATOGRAPHY.   Anal.
       Chem. 30, 1384-87 (1958).

539.   Boggus, J. D. and Adams, N. G.   GAS CHROMATOGRAPHY
       FOR TRACE ANALYSIS, Anal. Chem. 30, 1471 (1958).

540.   Bohemen, J. and Purnell, J. H.   SOME APPLICATIONS
       OF THEORY IN THE ATTAINMENT OF HIGH COLUMN
       EFFICIENCIES IN GAS-LIQUID CHROMATOGRAPHY,
       See ref. 556.

541.   Bohemen, J. and Purnell, J. H.   BEHAVIOUR OF KATHAR-
       OMETERS FOR GAS CHROMATOGRAPHY IN CARRIER
       GASES OF LOW THERMAL CONDUCTIVITY.   J. Appl.
       Chem. 8, 433-39 (1958).

542.   Bosanquet, C. H.   THE DIFFUSION AT A FRONT IN GAS
       CHROMATOGRAPHY, See ref. 556.

543.   Bovijn, L. , Pirotte, J. and Berger, A.   DETERMINATION
       OF HYDROGEN IN WATER BY MEANS OF GAS CHROMA-
       TOGRAPHY, See ref. 556.

544.   Brenner, N. and Coates, V. J.   MOLECULAR SIEVES AS
       SUBTRACTORS IN GAS CHROMATOGRAPHIC ANALYSIS.
       Nature 181, 1401-02 (1958).

545.   Brenner, N. and Hausdorff, H.   A COMPREHENSIVE
       STUDY OF INSTRUMENTATION FOR GAS CHROMATOG-

RAPHY, ISA Proceedings; 1958 Natl. Symp. on Instrumental Methods of Analysis, Houston, Texas, May 1958.

546. Burk, M. C. and Karasek, F. W. A DATA CONVERTER TO ADAPT CHROMATOGRAPHIC ANALYZERS FOR AUTOMATIC PROCESS CONTROL, ISA Proceedings; Natl. Symp. on Instrumental Methods of Analysis, Houston, Texas, May 1958.

547. Carle, D. W. and Johns, T. DESIGN AND APPLICATION OF PREPARATIVE SCALE GAS CHROMATOGRAPHY, ISA Proceedings; 1958 Natl. Symp. on Instrumental Methods of Analysis, Houston, Texas, May 1958.

548. Carruthers, W., Johnstone, R. A. W. and Plimmer, J. R. GAS-LIQUID PARTITION CHROMATOGRAPHY OF MIXTURES OF ARYL METHYL ESTERS, Chem. & Ind. (London) 1958, 331.

549. Cheshire, J. D. and Scott, R. P. W. GAS CHROMATOGRAPHY: EFFECT OF SUPPORT SIZE AND PROPORTION OF LIQUID PHASE ON COLUMN EFFICIENCY, J. Inst. Petrol. 44, 74-79 (1958).

550. Clough, K. H. CONTROL OF OPERATING PARAMETERS IN GAS CHROMATOGRAPHY AT VARIABLE TEMPERATURES, Paper presented at Southeastern Regional Meeting ACS, Gainesville, Florida, December 1958.

551. Coates, V. J., Noebels, H. J. and Fagerson, I. S. GAS CHROMATOGRAPHY. A Symposium Held Under the Auspices of the Analysis Instrumentation Division of the Instrument Society of America, East Lansing, Michigan, August 1957. Academic Press, New York, 1958.

552. Coleman, H. J., Thompson, C. J., Ward, C. C. and Rall, H. T. IDENTIFICATION OF LOW-BOILING SULFUR COMPOUNDS IN AGHA JARI CRUDE OIL BY GAS-LIQUID CHROMATOGRAPHY, Anal. Chem. 30, 1592 (1958).

553. Craig, B. M. and Murty, N. L. SEPARATION OF SATURATED AND UNSATURATED FATTY ACID ESTERS BY GAS-LIQUID CHROMATOGRAPHY. Can. J. Chem. 36, 1297-1302 (1958).

554.   Cremer, E. and Roselius, L.   GAS CHROMATOGRAPHY.
       Z. angew. Chem. 70, 42-50 (1958).

555.   Davis, A. D. and Howard, G. A.   THERMISTOR DETEC-
       TORS IN GAS CHROMATOGRAPHY. J. Appl. Chem. 8,
       183-86 (1958).

556.   Desty, D. H.   GAS CHROMATOGRAPHY. Proceedings of
       the Second Symposium on Gas Chromatography held in
       Amsterdam May 1958; Academic Press, New York, and
       Butterworths Scientific Publications, London, 1958.

557.   Desty, D. H.   COLUMN PACKINGS FOR GAS CHROMATOG-
       RAPHY, Nature 181, 604 (1958).

558.   Desty, D. H. , Godfrey, F. M. and Harbourn, C. L. A.
       OPERATING DATA ON TWO STATIONARY PHASE SUP-
       PORTS.   See ref. 556.

559.   De Wet, W. J. and Pretorius, V.   SOME FACTORS INFLU-
       ENCING THE EFFICIENCY OF GAS-LIQUID PARTITION
       CHROMATOGRAPHY COLUMN, Anal. Chem. 30, 325
       (1958).

560.   Dewhurst, H. A.   RADIATION CHEMISTRY OF ORGANIC
       COMPOUNDS. II. n-HEXANE. J. Phys. Chem. 62,
       15-20 (1958).

561.   Dietrich, P. and Mercier, D.   CHROMATOGRAPHIC
       IDENTIFICATION OF PYRAZINE BASES, J. Chromatog-
       raphy 1, 67 (1958).

562.   Dijkstra, G. and de Goey, J.   THE USE OF COATED
       CAPILLARIES AS COLUMNS FOR GAS CHROMATOG -
       RAPHY, See ref. 556.

563.   Domange, L. and Longuevalle, S.   USE OF GAS-LIQUID
       PARTITION CHROMATOGRAPHY. ANALYSIS OF OIL OF
       EUCALYPTUS, MENTHOL AND VARIOUS MEDICANTS.
       Comp. rend. 247, 209-11 (1958).

564.   Drew, C. M. , Schowen, R. L. and Smith, S. R.   NAVORD
       REPORT 5809, February 1958.

565.   Dupire, F. and Botquin, G.   L'ANALYSE QUALITATIVE

ET QUANTITATIVE DES HUILES LOURDES DE GOUDRON
PAR CHROMATOGRAPHIC. GAZEUSE, Anal. Chim. Acta
18, 282 (1958).

566. Eggertsen, F. T. and Knight, H. S. GAS CHROMATOG-
      RAPHY. EFFECT OF TYPE AND AMOUNT OF SOLVENT
      ON ANALYSES OF SATURATED HYDROCARBONS, Anal.
      Chem. 30, 15-19 (1958).

567. Eggertsen, F. T. and Groennings, S. DETERMINATION
      OF FIVE TO SEVEN CARBON SATURATES BY GAS
      CHROMATOGRAPHY, Anal. Chem. 30, 20-24 (1958).

568. Eggertsen, F. T. and Nelsen, F. M. GAS CHROMATO-
      GRAPHIC ANALYSIS OF ENGINE EXHAUST AND ATMOS-
      PHERE. DETERMINATION OF C_2 TO C_5 HYDROCARBONS,
      Anal. Chem. 30, 1040 (1958).

569. Ellis, J. F. and Iveson, G. THE APPLICATION OF GAS-
      LIQUID CHROMATOGRAPHY TO THE ANALYSIS OF
      VOLATILE HALOGEN AND INTERHALOGEN COMPOUNDS,
      See ref. 556.

570. Evans, D. E. M., Massingham, W. F., Stacey, M. and
      Tatlow, J. C. PREPARATIVE-SCALE GAS CHROMATOG-
      RAPHY, Nature 182, 591-92 (1958).

571. Felton, H. R. and Buehler, A. A. HIGH TEMPERATURE
      THERMAL CONDUCTIVITY CELL. Anal. Chem. 30, 1163
      (1958).

572. Fox, J. E. GAS CHROMATOGRAPHIC ANALYSIS OF
      ALCOHOL AND CERTAIN OTHER VOLATILES IN BIO-
      LOGICAL MATERIAL FOR FORENSIC PURPOSES.
      Proc. Soc. Exptl. Biol. Med. 97, 236-37 (1958).

573. Franc, J. and Jokl, J. SPECTROCHROMATOGRAPHY.
      I. DETERMINATION OF ISOMERIC XYLENES BY GAS
      LIQUID CHROMATOGRAPHY, Chem. listy 52, 276-82
      (1958).

574. Gimblett, F. G. R. CHROMATOGRAPHIC SEPARATION
      OF PHOSPHONITRILIC CHLORIDES BY VAPOR-PHASE
      TECHNIQUES, Chem. & Ind. (London) 1958, 365-66.

575. Glew, D. N. and Young, D. M. STOPCOCK FOR GAS CHROMATOGRAPHY. Anal. Chem. 30, 1890 (1958).

576. Glueckauf, E. THEORY OF CHROMATOGRAPHY, PART XII. CHROMATOGRAPHY OF HIGHLY RADIOACTIVE GASES, See ref. 556.

577. Golay, M. J. E. THEORY OF CHROMATOGRAPHY IN OPEN AND COATED TUBULAR COLUMNS WITH ROUND AND RECTANGULAR CROSS-SECTIONS, See ref. 556.

578. Gordon, S. , Van Dyken, A. R. and Doumani, T. F. IDENTIFICATION OF PRODUCTS IN THE RADIOLYSIS OF LIQUID BENZENE. J. Phys. Chem. 62, 20-24 (1958).

579. Grant, D. W. AN EMISSIVITY DETECTOR FOR GAS CHROMATOGRAPHY, See ref. 556.

580. Gray, F. B. , Jr. RELIABILITY OF GAS CHROMATOG-RAPHY AS AN ANALYTICAL FIELD TOOL, ISA Proceed-ings; Natl. Symp. on Instrumental Methods of Analysis, Houston, Texas, May 1958.

581. Gregg, S. J. and Stock, R. SORPTION ISOTHERMS AND CHROMATOGRAPHIC BEHAVIOR OF VAPOURS, See ref. 556.

582. Greene, S. A. and Pust, H. THE DETERMINATION OF HEATS OF ADSORPTION BY GAS-SOLID CHROMATOG-RAPHY. J. Phys. Chem. 62, 55-58 (1958).

583. Greene, S. A. and Pust, H. THE DETERMINATION OF NITROGEN DIOXIDE BY GAS-SOLID CHROMATOGRAPHY, Anal. Chem. 30, 1039 (1958).

584. Guild, L. , Bingham, S. and Aul, F. BASE LINE CONTROL IN GAS-LIQUID CHROMATOGRAPHY, See ref. 556.

585. Hamilton, C. H. and Meyer, R. A. MICROLITER SYRINGES FOR SAMPLE INTRODUCTION, ISA Proceedings; Natl. Symp. on Instrumental Methods of Analysis, Houston, Texas, May 1958.

586. Harley, J. , Nel, W. and Pretorius, V. FLAME IONIZA-TION DETECTOR FOR GAS CHROMATOGRAPHY, Nature

181, 177-78 (1958).

587. Harrison, G. F. , Knight, P. , Kelley, R. P. and Heath,
      M. T. THE USE OF MULTIPLE COLUMNS AND PRO-
      GRAMMED COLUMN HEATING IN THE ANALYSIS OF
      WIDE-BOILING RANGE HALOGENATED HYDROCARBON
      SAMPLES, See ref. 556.

588. Haskin, J. F. , Warren, G. W. , Priestley, L. J. , Jr. and
      Yarborough, V. A. GAS CHROMATOGRAPHY. ANALYSIS
      OF CONSTITUENTS IN THE STUDY OF AZEOTROPES,
      Anal. Chem. 30, 217-18 (1958).

589. Haslam, J. , Hamilton, J. B. and Jeffs, A. R. DETERMINA-
      TION OF POLY (ETHYL ESTERS) IN METHYL METHAC-
      RYLATE COPOLYMERS, Analyst 83, 66-71 (1958).

590. Haslam, J. and Jeffs, A. R. APPLICATION OF GAS-
      LIQUID CHROMATOGRAPHY. THE EXAMINATION OF
      SOLVENTS FROM PLASTIC ADHESIVES, Analyst 83, 455
      (1958).

591. Hausdorff, H. H. and Brenner, N. GAS CHROMATOG-
      RAPHY. Oil Gas J. 56, 73-75 (June 30, 1958); ibid. 122-
      124 (July 7); ibid. 86-88 (July 21); ibid. 89-90, 93-96 (Aug.
      4).

592. Hooimeijer, J. , Kwantes, A. and Van de Craats, F. THE
      AUTOMATIZATION OF GAS CHROMATOGRAPHY, See
      ref. 556.

593. Hughes, R. B. VOLATILE AMINES OF HERRING FISH.
      Nature 181, 1281 (1958).

594. Irvine, L. and Mitchell, T. J. GAS-LIQUID CHROMATOG-
      RAPHY. I. RETENTION VOLUME DATA OF CERTAIN
      TAR ACIDS, J. Appl. Chem. 8, 3-6 (1958).

595. Irvine, L. and Mitchell, T. J. GAS-LIQUID CHROMATOG-
      RAPHY. II. ANALYSIS OF THE ALKALI EXTRACT OF
      A LOW TEMPERATURE COAL TAR. J. Appl. Chem. 8,
      425-32 (1958).

596. Janak, J. and Komers, R. EVALUATION OF SOME
      SUGARS AS STATIONARY PHASES FOR SEPARATION OF
      PHENOLS BY GAS CHROMATOGRAPHY, See ref. 556.

597.   Jennings, E. C. , Jr. , Curran, T. D. and Edwards, D. G.
       GAS LIQUID PARTITION CHROMATOGRAPHY. DETER-
       MINATION OF 2, 6-DI-TERT-BUTYL-p-CRESOL ON
       ANTIOXIDANT TREATED PAPERBOARD, Anal. Chem.
       30, 1946 (1958).

598.   Johnson, H. W. and Stross, F. H. TERMS AND UNITS
       IN GAS CHROMATOGRAPHY, Anal. Chem. 30, 1586 (1958).

599.   Jones, J. H. , Ritchie, C. D. and Nernburger, S. H. THE
       DETERMINATION OF NAIL LACQUER SOLVENTS BY
       GAS-LIQUID CHROMATOGRAPHY, J. Assoc. Offic. Agr.
       Chemists 41, 673 (1958).

600.   Jones, W. L. and Kieselbach, R. UNITS OF MEASURE-
       MENT IN GAS CHROMATOGRAPHY, Anal. Chem. 30,
       1590 (1958).

601.   Karr, C. , Jr. , Brown, P. M. , Estep, P. A. and Humphrey,
       G. L. IDENTIFICATION AND DETERMINATION OF LOW-
       BOILING PHENOLS IN LOW TEMPERATURE COAL TAR.
       Anal. Chem. 30, 1413-16 (1958).

602.   Kerr, J. A. and Trotman-Dickenson, A. F. ADSORBENTS
       FOR ALDEHYDES AND OLEFINS. Nature 182, 466 (1958).

603.   Knight, H. S. GAS CHROMATOGRAPHY OF OLEFINS.
       DETERMINATION OF PENTENES AND HEXENES IN
       GASOLINE, Anal. Chem. 30, 9-14 (1958).

604.   Knight, H. S. GAS-LIQUID CHROMATOGRAPHY OF
       HYDROXYL AND AMINO COMPOUNDS. PRODUCTION
       OF SYMMETRICAL PEAKS, Anal. Chem. 30, 2030 (1958).

605.   Kovats, E. , Simon, W. and Heilbronner, E. PROGRAM
       CONTROLLED GAS CHROMATOGRAPHY FOR PREPARA-
       TIVE SEPARATION OF ORGANIC COMPOUNDS, Helv.
       Chim. Acta 41, 275-88 (1958).

606.   Kwantes, A. and Rijnders, G. W. A. THE DETERMINATION
       OF ACTIVITY COEFFICIENTS AT INFINTE DILUTION BY
       GAS-LIQUID CHROMATOGRAPHY, See ref. 556.

607.   Langer, S. H. , Zahn, C. and Pantazoplos, G. GAS-LIQUID
       CHROMATOGRAPHIC RESOLUTION OF m- AND p - XYL-

ENE: TETRAHALOPHTHALATE PHASES. Chem. & Ind. (London) 1958, 1145-47.

608.   Liberti, A. and Cartoni, G.P. ANALYSIS OF ESSENTIAL OILS BY GAS CHROMATOGRAPHY, See ref. 556.

609.   Liberti, A., Cartoni, G.P. and Pallotta, U. VAPOR PHASE CHROMATOGRAPHY OF METHYL ESTERS OF FATTY ACIDS AND THEIR QUANTITATIVE DETERMINA- TION BY AUTOMATIC COULOMETRY. Ann. Chim.(Rome) 48, 40-49 (1958).

610.   Lipsky, S.R. and Landowne, R.A. NEW PARTITION AGENT FOR USE IN THE RAPID SEPARATION OF FATTY ACID ESTERS BY GAS-LIQUID CHROMATOGRAPHY, Biochim et Biophys. Acta 27, 666-67 (1958) (in English).

611.   Littlewood, B. AN EXAMINATION OF COLUMN EFFI- CIENCY IN GAS-LIQUID CHROMATOGRAPHY, USING COLUMNS OF WETTED GLASS BEADS, See ref. 556.

612.   Lovelock, J.E. MEASUREMENT OF LOW VAPOUR CON- CENTRATIONS BY COLLISION WITH EXCITED RARE GAS ATOMS, Nature 181, 1460 (1958).

613.   Lovelock, J.E. A SENSITIVE DETECTOR FOR GAS CHROMATOGRAPHY, J. Chromatography 1, 34 (1958).

614.   Lowe, A.E. and Moore, D. SCINTILLATION COUNTER FOR MEASURING RADIOACTIVITY OF VAPOURS, Nature 182, 133-34 (1958).

615.   Mackay,   Discussion, Ref. 551, p. 65.

616.   Madison, J. ANALYSIS OF FIXED AND CONDENSABLE GASES BY TWO-STAGE GAS CHROMATOGRAPHY, Anal. Chem. 30, 1859 (1958).

617.   Mattick, L.R., Moyer, J.C. and Schollenberger, R.S. A VOLATILE ACIDIC FLAVOR COMPONENT OF APPLE SAUCE, Food Technology 12, 613-15 (1958).

618.   McFadden, W.H. USE OF MIXED STATIONARY LIQUIDS IN GAS-LIQUID CHROMATOGRAPHY, Anal. Chem. 30, 479 (1958).

619. McWilliam, I. G. and Dewar, R. A. FLAME IONIZATION
      DETECTOR FOR GAS CHROMATOGRAPHY,   See ref.
      556.

620. McWilliam, I. G. and Dewar, R. A. FLAME IONIZATION
      DETECTOR FOR GAS CHROMATOGRAPHY, Nature 181,
      760 (1958).

621. Miettinen, J. K. GAS CHROMATOGRAPHY - A REVIEW.
      Suomen Kemistilehti 31A, 149-64 (1958).

622. Moussebois, C. and Duyckaerts, G. THE RADIOCHRO-
      MATOGRAPHIC GASES. J. Chromatography 1, 200-01
      (1958).

623. Nelsen, F. M. and Eggertsen, F. T. DETERMINATION OF
      SURFACE AREA. ADSORPTION MEASUREMENTS BY A
      CONTINUOUS FLOW METHOD. Anal. Chem. 30, 1387-90
      (1958).

624. Nogare, S. Dal and Bennett, C. E.   PROGRAMMED
      TEMPERATURE GAS CHROMATOGRAPHY. Anal. Chem.
      30, 1157-58 (1958).

625. Nogare, S. Dal and Safranski, L. W. HIGH TEMPERATURE
      GAS CHROMATOGRAPHY APPARATUS, Anal. Chem. 30,
      895 (1958).

626. Norman, R. O. C. 2, 4, 7-TRINITROFLUORENONE AS A
      STATIONARY PHASE IN GAS CHROMATOGRAPHY, Proc.
      Chem. Soc. 1958, 151; C. A. 52, 17892 (1958).

627. Nystrom, R. F. and Berger, C. R. A. SEPARATION OF
      ALLYLIC BROMIDES WITHOUT ISOMERIZATION BY GAS
      CHROMATOGRAPHIC TECHNIQUES. Chem. & Ind. (Lon-
      don) 1958, 559-60.

628. O'Brien, L. and Scholly, P. R. GAS CHROMATOGRAPHIC
      SEPARATION OF META- AND PARA-XYLENES IN ARO-
      MATIC MIXTURES. Nature 181, 1794 (1958).

629. Ogilvie, J. L. , Simmons, M. C. and Hinds, G. P. , Jr.
      EXPLORATORY STUDIES OF HIGH TEMPERATURE GAS-
      LIQUID CHROMATOGRAPHY, Anal. Chem. 30, 25-27 (1958).

630. Orr, C.H. and Callen, J.E. SEPARATION OF POLYUN-
SATURATED FATTY ACID METHYL ESTERS BY GAS
CHROMATOGRAPHY, J. Am. Chem. Soc. 80, 249 (1958).

631. Pietsch, H. DETERMINATION OF VERY SMALL AMOUNTS
OF OXYGEN, CARBON MONOXIDE, METHANE, AND
NITROGEN IN PUREST ETHYLENE BY ADSORPTION
CHROMATOGRAPHY, Erdöl u. Kohle 11, 157-59 (1958).

632. Pitkethly, R.C. LOW PRESSURE DISCHARGE DETEC-
TORS, Anal. Chem. 30, 1309 (1958).

633. Podbielniak, W.J. and Preston, S.T. THE FUTURE POS-
SIBILITIES OF GAS CHROMATOGRAPHY, Gas 34, 119-20,
122, 126 (1958).

634. Primavesi, G.R., Oldham, G.F. and Thompson, R.J.
STUDY OF THE HYDROGEN FLAME DETECTOR USING
NITROGEN AS CARRIER GAS, See ref. 556.

635. Quin, L.D. and Hobbs, M.E. ANALYSIS OF THE NON-
VOLATILE ACIDS IN CIGARETTE SMOKE BY GAS CHRO-
MATOGRAPHY OF THEIR METHYL ESTERS, Anal. Chem.
30, 1400 (1958).

636. Reed, T.M., III, GAS-LIQUID PARTITION CHROMATOG-
RAPHY OF FLUOROCARBONS, Anal. Chem. 30, 221-27
(1958).

637. Rhoades, J.W. SAMPLING METHOD FOR ANALYSIS OF
COFFEE VOLATILES BY GAS CHROMATOGRAPHY,
Food Research 23, (3), 254 (1958).

638. Riesz, P. and Wilzbach, K.E. LABELING OF SOME C_6
HYDROCARBONS BY EXPOSURE TO TRITIUM. J. Phys.
Chem. 62, 6-9 (1958).

639. Schuck, E.A., Ford, H.W. and Stephens, E.R. AIR
POLLUTION EFFECTS OF IRRADIATED AUTOMOBILE
EXHAUST AS RELATED TO FUEL COMPOSITION. Air
Pollution Foundation (San Marino, Calif.) Report No. 26,
1958.

640. Scott, R.P.W. THE CONSTRUCTION OF HIGH-EFFI-
CIENCY COLUMNS FOR THE SEPARATION OF HYDRO-

CARBONS, See ref. 556.

641.   Simmons, M.C. and Snyder, L.R. TWO STAGE GAS-
       LIQUID CHROMATOGRAPHY, Anal. Chem. 30, 32-35
       (1958).

642.   Smith, R.N., Swinehart, J. and Lesnini, D.G. CHROMA-
       TOGRAPHIC ANALYSIS OF GAS MIXTURES CONTAINING
       NITROGEN, NITROUS OXIDE, NITRIC OXIDE, CARBON
       MONOXIDE AND CARBON DIOXIDE, Anal. Chem. 30,
       1217 (1958).

643.   Spencer, C.F. and Johnson, J.F. PUNCHED CARD
       STORAGE OF GAS CHROMATOGRAPHIC DATA, Anal.
       Chem. 30, 893 (1958).

644.   Spencer, C.F., Baumann, Fred and Johnson, J.F. GAS
       ODORANTS ANALYSIS BY GAS CHROMATOGRAPHY,
       Anal. Chem. 30, 1473 (1958).

645.   Strain, H. CHROMATOGRAPHY. ANALYSIS BY DIF-
       FERENTIAL MIGRATION, Anal. Chem. 30, 620-29 (1958).

646.   Stuve, W. A SIMPLE KATHAROMETER FOR USE WITH
       THE COMBUSTION METHOD, See ref. 556.

647.   Sverak, J. and Reiser, P.L. GAS-CHROMATOGRAPHIC
       DETECTION OF SMALL AMOUNTS OF ETHER IN ETHYL-
       ENE, Mikrochim, Acta (1), 159 (1958).

648.   Tarbes, H. and Bonnet, E. CHROMATOGRAPHIC
       ANALYSIS OF HYDROCARBONS. J. usines gaz. 82,
       261-66 (1958).

649.   Tenney, H.M. SELECTIVITY OF VARIOUS LIQUID SUB-
       STRATES USED IN GAS CHROMATOGRAPHY, Anal.
       Chem. 30, 2-8 (1958).

650.   Timms, D.G., Konrath, H.J. and Chirnside, R.C. THE
       DETERMINATION OF IMPURITIES IN CARBON DIOXIDE
       BY GAS CHROMATOGRAPHY WITH SPECIAL REFERENCE
       TO COOLANT GAS FOR NUCLEAR REACTORS, Analyst
       83, 600 (1958).

651.   Troupe, R.A. and Golner, J.J. PROCESS CONTROL

METHODS IN THE CHLORINATION OF BENZENE. Anal.
Chem. 30, 129-31 (1958).

652. Tuey, G. A. P. GAS CHROMATOGRAPHY AND ITS
APPLICATION TO PERFUMERY MATERIALS, Soap,
Perfum. Cosm. 31, 353 (1958).

653. Turner, D. W. A ROBUST BUT SENSITIVE DETECTOR
FOR GAS-LIQUID CHROMATOGRAPHY, Nature 181, 1265
(1958).

654. Van de Craats, F. SOME QUANTITATIVE ASPECTS OF
THE CHROMATOGRAPHIC ANALYSIS OF GAS MIXTURES,
USING THERMAL CONDUCTIVITY AS DETECTION METH-
OD, See ref. 556.

655. Vertalier, S. and Martin, F. SELECTIVE MICRODETER-
MINATION OF ALKOXY GROUPS BY GAS-LIQUID CHRO-
MATOGRAPHY, Chim. anal. 40, 80-86 (1958).

656. West, P. W. , Sen, B. and Gibson, N. A. GAS-LIQUID
CHROMATOGRAPHIC ANALYSIS APPLIED TO AIR POL-
LUTION. SAMPLING, Anal. Chem. 30, 1390 (1958).

657. White, D. and Cowan, C. T. SYMMETRICAL ELUTION
CURVES IN ADSORPTION CHROMATOGRAPHY, See ref.
556.

658. White, D. and Cowan, C. T. THE SORPTION PROPERTIES
OF DIMETHYLDIOCTADECYL AMMONIUM BENTONITE
USING GAS CHROMATOGRAPHY. Trans. Faraday Soc.
54, 557-61 (1958).

659. Whitham, B. T. USE OF MOLECULAR SIEVES IN GAS
CHROMATOGRAPHY FOR THE DETERMINATION OF
THE NORMAL PARAFFINS IN PETROLEUM FRACTIONS.
Nature 182, 391-92 (1958).

660. Wolfgang, R. and Rowland, F. S. RADIOASSAY BY GAS
CHROMATOGRAPHY OF TRITIUM- AND CARBON-14-
LABELED COMPOUNDS, Anal. Chem. 30, 903 (1958).

661. Young, J. R. THE "FAMILY PLOT" OF RETENTION
VOLUMES FOR ALKYL KETONES ON DINONYL PHTHAL-
ATE. Chem. & Ind. (London) 1958, 594-95.

662.   Zinn, T.L., Baker, W.J. and Wall, R.F.   THE USE OF
       HYDROGEN AS A CARRIER GAS IN PROCESS GAS CHRO-
       MATOGRAPHY, ISA Proceedings; Natl. Symp. on Instru-
       mental Methods of Analysis, Houston, Texas, May 1958.

663.   Zlatkis, A.   RESOLUTION OF ISOMERIC HEXANES BY
       GAS CHROMATOGRAPHY, Anal. Chem. 30, 332 (1958).

664.   Zlatkis, A., O'Brien, L. and Scholly, P.R.   GAS CHRO-
       MATOGRAPHIC SEPARATION OF META- AND PARA-
       XYLENES IN AROMATIC MIXTURES.   Nature 181, 1794
       (1958).

665.   Zlatkis, A. and Oro, J.F.   AMINO ACID ANALYSIS BY
       REACTOR-GAS CHROMATOGRAPHY.   Anal. Chem. 30,
       1156 (1958).

666.   Zlatkis, A. and Ridgway, J.A.   A METHANE-CONVER-
       SION DETECTOR FOR GAS CHROMATOGRAPHY. Nature
       182, 130-31 (1958).

                              1959

667.   Anderson, D.M.W.   APPLICATIONS OF INFRARED
       SPECTROSCOPY: THE IDENTIFICATION AND DETER-
       MINATION OF GAS-CHROMATOGRAPHIC FRACTIONS.
       Analyst 84, 50-55 (1959).

668.   Barber, D.W., Phillips, C.S.G., Tusa, G.F. and Verdin,
       A. THE CHROMATOGRAPHY OF GASES AND VAPOURS.
       PART VI. USE OF STEARATES OF BIVALENT MANGA-
       NESE, COBALT, NICKEL, COPPER, AND ZINC AS COL-
       UMN LIQUIDS IN GAS CHROMATOGRAPHY. J. Chem.
       Soc. 1959, 18-29.

669.   Barnard, J.A. and Hughes, H.W.D.   ANALYSIS OF LIGHT
       HYDROCARBON GAS MIXTURES, Nature 183, 250 (1959).

670.   Bosanquet, C.H.   PEAK DIMENSIONS IN GAS CHROMA-
       TOGRAPHY. Nature 183, 252-53 (1959).

671.   Brace, R.O.   BECKMAN INSTRUMENTS, FULLERTON,
       CALIFORNIA, private communication.

672.   Craig, B.M., Mallard, T.M. and Hoffman, L.L.   COL-

LECTION UNIT FOR GAS-LIQUID CHROMATOGRAPHY
UNDER REDUCED PRESSURE. Anal. Chem. 31, 319-20
(1959).

673.   Desty, D.H., Goldup, A. and Swanton, W.T.   SEPARA-
        TION OF m-XYLENE AND p-XYLENE BY GAS CHROMA-
        TOGRAPHY. Nature 183, 107-08 (1959).

674.   Greene, S.A.   GAS-SOLID CHROMATOGRAPHIC ANALY-
        SIS OF FRACTIONS FROM AIR RECTIFICATION COLUMNS.
        Anal. Chem. 31, 480 (1959).

675.   Hanson, D.N. and Maimoni, A.   GAS BLENDING APPA-
        RATUS. Anal. Chem. 31, 158-59 (1959).

676.   Hardy, C.J. and Pollard, F.H.   REVIEW OF GAS-LIQUID
        CHROMATOGRAPHY. J. Chromatography 2, 1-43 (1959).

677.   Harris, B.L.   ADSORPTION. Ind. Eng. Chem. 51, 340-
        343 (1959).

678.   Harris, W.E. and McFadden, W.H.   SELECTIVE REAC-
        TIVITY IN GAS LIQUID CHROMATOGRAPHY. DETER-
        MINATION OF 2-BROMOBUTANE AND 1-BROMO-2-METH-
        YLPROPANE. Anal. Chem. 31, 114-17 (1959).

679.   Heaton, W.B. and Wentworth, J.T.   EXHAUST GAS ANALY-
        SIS BY GAS CHROMATOGRAPHY COMBINED WITH INFRA-
        RED DETECTION. Anal. Chem. 31, 349-57 (1959).

680.   Johnson, H.W., Jr. and Stross, F.H. GAS-LIQUID CHRO-
        MATOGRAPHY. DETERMINATION OF COLUMN EFFI-
        CIENCY. Anal. Chem. 31, 357-65 (1959).

681.   Johnstone, R.A.W. and Douglas, A.G.   A DETECTOR
        FOR GAS-LIQUID CHROMATOGRAPHY. Chem. & Ind.
        (London) 1959, 154.

682.   Kyryacos, G., Menapace, H.R. and Boord, C.E.   GAS
        LIQUID CHROMATOGRAPHIC ANALYSIS OF SOME OXY-
        GENATED PRODUCTS OF COOL-FLAME COMBUSTION.
        Anal. Chem. 31, 222-25 (1959).

683.   LaFrance, D.S.   SHELL DEVELOPMENT CORP.,
        EMERYVILLE, CALIFORNIA, private communication.

684. Lesser, J.M. DEVICE FOR ISOLATION OF COMPONENTS
      SEPARATED BY GAS CHROMATOGRAPHY. Anal. Chem.
      31, 484 (1959).

685. Link, W., Hickman, H.M. and Morrissette, R.A. GAS
      LIQUID CHROMATOGRAPHY OF FATTY DERIVATIVES.
      I. SEPARATION OF HOMOLOGOUS SERIES OF a-OLE-
      FINS, n-HYDROCARBONS, n-NITRILES AND n-ALCOHOLS.
      J. Am. Oil Chem. Soc. 36, 20-23 (1959).

686. Messner, A.E., Rosie, D.M. and Argabright, P.A.
      CORRELATION OF THERMAL CONDUCTIVITY CELL
      RESPONSE WITH MOLECULAR WEIGHT AND STRUCTURE.
      Anal. Chem. 31, 230-33 (1959).

687. Musgrave, W.K.R. THERMISTOR DETECTORS IN GAS
      CHROMATOGRAPHY. Chem. & Ind. (London) 1959, 46.

688. Ormerod, E.C. and Scott, R.P.W. GAS CHROMATOG-
      RAPHY OF POLAR COMPOUNDS USING A NON-POLAR
      LIQUID PHASE. J. Chromatography 2, 65-68 (1959).

689. Pierotti, G.J., Deal, C.H. and Derr, E.L. ACTIVITY
      COEFFICIENTS AND MOLECULAR STRUCTURE. Ind.
      Eng. Chem. 51, 95-102 (1959).

690. Porter, R.S. and Johnson, J.F. CIRCULAR GAS CHRO-
      MATOGRAPH. Nature 183, 391-92 (1959).

691. Reed, T.M., Walter, J.F., Cecil, R.R. and Dresdner, R.D.
      QUANTITY PURIFICATION OF FLUOROCARBONS BY
      GAS-LIQUID CHROMATOGRAPHY. Ind. Eng. Chem. 51,
      271-74 (1959).

692. Schmauch, L.J. RESPONSE TIME AND FLOW SENSITIV-
      ITY OF DETECTORS FOR GAS CHROMATOGRAPHY. Anal.
      Chem. 31, 225-30 (1959).

693. Stoffel, W., Chu, F. and Ahrens, E.H., Jr. ANALYSIS
      OF LONG-CHAIN FATTY ACIDS BY GAS LIQUID CHRO-
      MATOGRAPHY. MICROMETHOD FOR PREPARATION
      OF METHYL ESTERS. Anal. Chem. 31, 307-08 (1959).

694. Tamaru, K. A CHROMATOGRAPHIC TECHNIQUE FOR
      STUDYING THE MECHANISM OF SURFACE CATALYSIS.

Nature 183, 319-20 (1959).

695.   Tonge, B. L. and Timms, D. G. USE OF MOLECULAR
        SIEVES AS GAS SAMPLERS. Chem. & Ind. (London)
        1959, 155-56.

696.   Vizard, G. S. and Wynne, A. DETERMINATION OF AR-
        GON AND OXYGEN BY GAS CHROMATOGRAPHY.
        Chem. & Ind. (London) 1959, 196-97.

697.   West, P. W., Sen, B. and Sant, B. R. DETERMINATION
        OF TOTAL GASEOUS POLLUTANTS IN ATMOSPHERE.
        Anal. Chem. 31, 399-401 (1959).

ADDENDA

698.   Golay, M. J. E. GAS CHROMATOGRAPHIC TERMS AND
        DEFINITIONS, Nature 182, 1146-47 (1958).

699.   Lipsky, S. R., Lovelock, J. E. and Landowne, R. A. THE
        USE OF HIGH EFFICIENCY CAPILLARY COLUMNS FOR
        THE SEPARATION OF CERTAIN cis-trans ISOMERS OF
        LONG CHAIN FATTY ACID ESTERS BY GAS CHROMA-
        TOGRAPHY. J. Am. Chem. Soc. 81, 1010 (1959).

700.   Greene, S. A. unpublished results.

701.   Cady, G. H. and Siegwarth, D. P. FRACTIONAL CODIS-
        TILLATION IN GAS CHROMATOGRAPHY APPARATUS.
        Anal. Chem. 31, 618-20 (1959).

702.   Franc, J. and Jokl, J. DETERMINATION OF XYLOL
        ISOMERS BY MEANS OF GAS-LIQUID CHROMATOG-
        RAPHY. Collection Czechoslov. Chem. Communs. 24,
        144-51 (1959).

703.   Frey, H. M. ANALYSIS OF HYDROCARBONS. Nature
        183, 743-44 (1959).

704.   Gohlke, R. S. TIME-OF-FLIGHT MASS SPECTROMETRY
        AND GAS-LIQUID PARTITION CHROMATOGRAPHY.
        Anal. Chem. 31, 535-41 (1959).

705.   Janak, J. and Novak, J. CHROMATOGRAPHIC SEMI-
        MICROANALYSIS OF GASES. XIV. THE DIRECT DE-

TERMINATION OF INDIVIDUAL VOLATILE PARAFFINS AND OLEFINS IN 1, 3-BUTADIENE. Collection Czechoslov. Chem. Communs. 24, 384-90 (1959).

706.   Janak, J. and Tesarik, K. CHROMATOGRAPHIC SEMI-MICROANALYSIS OF GASES. XV. THE AUTOMATION OF GAS CHROMATOGRAPHIC INSTRUMENTS. Collection Czechoslov. Chem. Communs. 24, 536-43 (1959).

707.   Schmauch, L. J. and Dinerstein, R. A. EFFECT OF CARRIER GAS ON THE SENSITIVITY OF A THERMAL-CONDUCTIVITY DETECTOR IN GAS CHROMATOGRAPHY. Nature 183, 673-74 (1959).

708.   Sokol, L. ANALYSIS OF PHENOL AND HYDROCARBONS WITH GAS-LIQUID CHROMATOGRAPHY. Collection Czechoslov. Chem. Communs. 24, 437-47 (1959).

709.   Thompson, A. E. A FLAME IONIZATION DETECTOR FOR GAS CHROMATOGRAPHY. J. Chromatography 2, 148-54 (1959).

710.   Zlatkis, A. and Lovelock, J. E. GAS CHROMATOGRAPHY OF HYDROCARBONS USING CAPILLARY COLUMNS AND IONIZATION DETECTORS. Anal. Chem. 31, 620-21 (1959).

INDEX

Adsorption isotherm (see
    Isotherm, adsorp-
    tion)
Analysis, air pollution, 95-
    96, 140-141
    qualitative, 136-142
    of mixtures, 140
    of solvent, 141-142
    quantitative, 142-150
    trace, 82, 95-96, 149

Bake out, procedure for,
    102-103
Benzene, 10, 26
    modification of carrier
    gas with, 64
n-Butane, heat of adsorp-
    tion of 32-33

Capillary columns, 19, 129
Carbon columns, 22, 34, 40
    48-49
Carbon dioxide, as carrier
    gas, 35, 117-118

Carbon number column, 73
Carrier gas, effect of, on
    retention time, 33-35
    on sensitivity, 38-39,
    120-121
    modification of to prevent
    tailing, 64, 67
    selection of, 17, 35-40,
    120-121
    thermal conductivity of,
    36-38
Charcoal columns (see Car-
    bon columns)
Column dimensions, 9, 60,
    83-84, 103-104, 110-
    111
Column packing, procedure
    for, 84-85, 102
Columns, mixed, 74, 80
    multiple, 73-74, 80, 96, 99
Combustors, copper dioxide,
    54-55, 143

Desty, D. H. , 131-133

Detector, flame tempera-
 ture, 131
 gas density balance, 118-
 119
 glow discharge tube, 129-
 130
 ionization, beta-ray, 130-
 131
 filament, 130
 flame, 132
 sensitivity of, 41-42, 124-
 127
 thermal conductivity, 119-
 124, 143
 temperature control of,
 105-106
Detector noise, elimination
 of, 54, 121-122, 129
Detectors, multiple, 140
Dimethylformamide column,
 53
Displacement analysis, description of, 5
 to prevent tailing, 64

Efficiency, column, definition of, 56
Elution analysis, description of, 6-7

Flow rate, control of, 40-41,
 106-109
 effect of, on efficiency, 44
 on peak area, 41-42
 on peak height, 41-42
 on retention time, 31, 43
 on separation, 43
 on time constant of de-
 tector, 127-129
 optimum, 14-15, 44-45
Frontal analysis, description of, 3

Gasoline, analysis of, 23,
 140-141
Golay columns (see Capil-
 lary columns)

Heat of adsorption, determination from GSC
 data, 32-37
Heat of solution, determination from GLC data,
 32-33
HETP, definition of, 12-13
High temperature columns,
 81, 105
Hydrogen, determination of,
 38-40
Hydrogen bonding, effect on
 selectivity, 10-26

Instruments, commercial,
 151-152
Integrators, automatic, 133-
 134
Isotherm, adsorption, 6-7,
 30, 63-64

James, A. T., 1, 47, 117-118
Janak, J., 117

Katharometer, (see Detector,
 thermal conductivity)

Lovelock, J. E., 130-131

Martin, A. J. P., 1, 8, 11, 28,
 47, 86, 99, 117, 136
Methane, retention time of,
 effect of carrier gas
 on, 35
Molecular Sieves, 23, 49-50,
 80

Overlapping peaks, 145-149

Partition coefficient, 25-27, 31-33, 98, 137
Peak area, measurement of, 133, 144-145
Peak areas, use in quantitative analysis, 142-149
Peak heights, use in quantitative analysis, 142
Performance Index, 19
Plate theory, 11-12, 44, 86
Plates (see Theoretical plates)
Polar columns, selectivity of, 10, 22, 69-71, 75-78
Pressure, effect on efficiency, 18, 81
Pressure drop in column, 15-16
  correction for, 47

Rate theory, 13-18, 44
Relative volatility, definition of, 21
  See also Separation factor
Retention time, 6, 12
  dependence of, on carrier gas, 33-35
  on flow rate, 31, 43
  on structure, 74-75
  on temperature, 31-33, 98-99
  plots of, 26-27, 78, 137-140
Retention volume, corrected for pressure drop, 46
  plots of (see Retention time, plots of)

Retention volume, specific (see Specific retention volume)

Sample size, effect on efficiency, 17, 61, 89
Sampling valves, 90-92
Separation factor, 9
Silica gel columns, 50-51
Silver nitrate-ethylene glycol columns, 10-11, 37
Specific retention volume, 26, 137
Standards, use of, 27, 69-71, 137, 144
Synge, R. L. M., 1, 8, 11, 28, 86
Syringes, micro, 92-95

Tailing, causes of, 63-64
  reduction of, 64-68, 71-73
Temperature, effect of, on peak shape, 62, 67-68
  on retention time, 31-33, 98-99
  maximum for various solvents, 52-53, 100
Temperature control, apparatus for, 103-115
  of detectors, 105-106
  programmed, 51, 106-115
  requirements for, 103, 109
Tenney, H. M., 78
Theoretical plate, definition of, 8
Theoretical plates, number of, calculation of 12, 44, 56
  requirements for, 9, 18-19, 24

Trace analysis (see Analysis, trace)

Van Deemter equation, 13-15, 44, 56-58
   test of, 17-18, 58-61

Weeping, 52-54, 100-102

m- and p-Xylenes, separation of, 11
o- and p-Xylenes, separation of, 44-45